RANGELAND MANAGEMENT FOR LIVESTOCK PRODUCTION

**University of Oklahoma
Press : Norman**

Rangeland Management for Livestock Production

HERSHEL M. BELL

This book is dedicated to
Jane, my wife, and Don and Jerry, my sons

Library of Congress Cataloging in Publication Data

Bell, Hershel M   1906–
    Rangeland management for livestock production.

    Bibliography: p.
    1. Range management.   I. Title.
SF85.B37   636.08'4   72–9274
ISBN 0–8061–1080–5

PREFACE

John J. Ingalls said, "Grass is the forgiveness of nature, her constant benediction. It yields no fruit in earth or air, and yet should its harvest fail for a single year, famine would depopulate the world."

These, the first and last statements of his eulogy on grass, are indicative of the significance he places on this benefaction of the earth. When grass is used and nurtured according to the precepts of the creator, its power to provide and to protect the basic resources of mankind are unsurpassed.

To say that grass is universal can be contradicted only when speaking of those segments of the earth where life-giving requirements of the environment are limited or non-existent. Wherever grass is found, its persistence is unceasing until the destructive forces of mankind, through procrastination, subdue its growth requirements.

With the Creation, there was grass. Through the ages, grass has persisted, but like all resources of the earth, it has reacted and responded to its environment. Doubtless, in the beginning there were various kinds of grass, and, then as now, they were fitted to environments that varied from one part of the world to another. Within these varied environments were ecological variations and influences that have resulted in the many differences among grasses as we know them today.

Management of grassland, or range management, is nothing more than man's responsibility to correlate the use and treatment of grass with its existing environmental growth requirements. In simple terminology, nature has provided the grass and the conditions under which it will grow and produce. If these conditions are allowed to exert their influence, optimum growth and production will result. But if these conditions are violated, or even disrupted, growth and production will be adversely affected.

Range management practices, and, to a very large extent, rangeland treatment practices, are designed to encourage the natural environmental elements necessary for grass growth and development.

These influences will vary from minor adjustments in the growth of plants to drastic treatment of the range. But the severity of treatment necessary to compensate for rangeland deterioration will depend on past grazing use. Therefore, range management is the criterion by which native rangeland is restored and maintained in its most productive state. Restoration and maintenance are the responsibility of the user of the range. When his management insures the production and most efficient use of the highest type of forage plants that can be grown, he will have fulfilled that responsibility.

Range was early identified as an association of noncultivated or native forage plants. Such areas were unsuitable for cultivation because of poor soil, topography, rainfall, location, or economic productivity.

More recently, the concept of range has embraced much more than plants that grow and animals that consume them. Range has come to be recognized as a complex, and is identified as an ecosystem, one that includes not only the soil and vegetation, but also the associated atmosphere, the water, and animal life. Vegetation components comprise the aggregate of plants, including fungi, algae, mosses, forbs, grasses, shrubs, and trees. The animal population includes man, domestic livestock, and the entire fauna above and below the ground. (Blaisdell, Duvall, Harris, Lloyd, and Reid, *Journal of Range Management.* Vol. 23, July 1970, No. 4.)

Further interpretation of a range recognizes its products as water, air, fish and other wildlife, forage for livestock, recreation, and such miscellaneous products as fruits and nuts, chemical compounds, and wood products.

Because these many entities of the range are significant, they should be included in any comprehensive treatise dealing with resources of the range in its entirety. This book, however, is not all-inclusive, but deals primarily with range forage production and domestic livestock that uses the range. Forage-consuming game animals are recognized as contributors to range use and enter into range management to that extent only.

Range management has become significant as a science during the past thirty to forty years. Although it came into being primarily through the work of the U.S. Forest Service, it also became a responsibility of other institutions and agencies, especially the U.S. Soil Conservation Service, as the need arose.

Through this comparatively short span of years, many varied techniques have been developed, redeveloped, revised, evaluated, and made available to operators of grazing lands. Unfortunately, these innovations have too often been piecemeal and not clearly understood; frequently they have been not completely appropriate and incompatible with ranching operations.

This publication is an attempt to present information and developments that contribute to range and livestock management and production, and to coordinate them into a practical guide for the student and the rancher.

The contents are supported primarily by experience gained in the Southern Plains portion of western rangelands.

ACKNOWLEDGMENTS

The author is deeply indebted to many individuals, agencies, and institutions for guidance, training, encouragement, and help in making this publication possible. The opportunity afforded to gain the knowledge, experience, and confidence in the field of range management has provided a most rewarding career.

Special appreciation is expressed to the USDA Soil Conservation Service and many co-workers, including F. G. Renner, B. W. Allred, Louis P. Merrill, J. C. Dykes, the late H. N. Smith, Dr. E. J. Dykster-huis, Robert E. Williams, Liter E. Spence, the late Eric A. Johnson, Arnold Heerwagen, H. L. Leithead, C. A. Rechenthin, Howard B. Passey, Joe B. Norris, A. T. Wilhite, R. J. Pederson, D. B. Polk, James E. "Bud" Smith, the late Odis J. Curry, the late R. M. Mil-hollin, C. E. Kingery, the late Neil Stidham, and many others.

Contributions to this endeavor from the Department of Range and Wildlife Management at Texas Technological University have been many and most helpful. Professor Joseph L. Schuster, chairman of that department, has been a motivating force and has made many direct contributions to the work. Both he and Professor John Hunter, of the department, were technical editors of the manuscript. Their thorough and constructive reviews contributed greatly to the presentation of the subject matter. Of equal significance is the wonderfully fine job done by Betty Jones, Patsy Shelton, and Veda Buckner, in typing the first draft of the manuscript. To these people at Texas Technological University, the author is sincerely grateful.

There are many others to whom credit and appreciation are due for their co-operation in the development of a technically sound, practical range management program. To name some of these people: Professor C. L. Leinweber, Professor Vernon Young (retired), A. H. Walker, Garlyn O. Hoffman, Bobby J. Ragsdale, Leo B. Merrill, Calvin C. Boykin, Wayne G. McCully, and Omer E. Sperry, all of

Texas A. & M. University; John L. Merrill, of Texas Christian University; Professor Francis M. Churchill, of Abilene Christian College; Professor Leroy J. Young, of Southwest Texas State University; Gerald W. Thomas, president, New Mexico State University; William J. Waldrip, manager, Spade Ranch Estate; and R. B. Dooley of Angelo State College.

Of no less importance, for their contributions and co-operation, are the many ranchers with whom the author has been associated through the years. To them go special thanks and good wishes.

Appreciation is extended to numerous representatives of the U.S. Soil Conservation Service in Texas, Louisiana, Colorado, and New Mexico for photographs; also to Professors Schuster and Dahl of Texas Technological University; and to rancher Ed Harrell of Claude, Texas. Thanks are extended to rancher Jack Douglas of Hale Center, Texas, for his art work.

In every worthwhile achievement there is that extra effort by one who has not only the ability but the devoted interest and perseverance to see the job through to completion. Credit goes to Mrs. Grace Roney of Hale Center, Texas, for the final editing and typing of the manuscript.

The one to whom the most gratitude, thanks, and appreciation are due, is my wife, Jane. Through many years she has been devoted, encouraging, persevering, tolerant, sacrificial, and enduring. Without these qualities, along with her untiring and loving care over my personal well-being, completion of this project would not have been possible.

Hale Center, Texas
November, 1972

HERSHEL M. BELL

CONTENTS

RANGELAND MANAGEMENT FOR LIVESTOCK PRODUCTION

Chapter 1

DEFINING RANGELAND
AND RANGE MANAGEMENT

The broad concept of rangeland as an important land use throughout the world. Its relationship to other uses of land. Technical and management differences between range and pasture lands. Recognition and explanation of the science of range management. The significance of reading the landscape of rangelands. Identification of the basic principles of range management. Factors that influence the grazing of rangelands.

Range is the primary resource of a ranching operation. It is land, usually in large areas, that supports a combination of native plants growing in association with each other as their growth requirements are influenced by soil, climate, and treatment. Such plants are generally those adapted to the environment and established there originally. Or they are plants with similar growth requirements, which have moved in as the original flora is eliminated.

In different parts of the country, variations in soil, climate, elevation, topography, and other factors cause variations in the kind of native vegetation found on rangelands. Also affected are the varieties of wild animals that occupy the area.

Though rangeland as a distinct land use is found throughout the world, it is most significant on the continents of Africa, Australia, North America, and South America. Wherever rangelands occur, they are generally unsuited for the production of cultivated crops with the existing culture and stage of development. They may occur as highly productive areas, or the productive capacity may grade downward to desertlike or even true desert conditions.

Almost from the beginning of civilized use of land, rangelands have been closely correlated with uses such as forest production, wildlife, recreation, and mineral deposits. With the advent of the U.S. Forest Service, greater significance was placed on these uses.

Administrative and developmental programs have been initiated to study uses separate from grazing.

In many instances, these programs have resulted in satisfactory dual uses of rangelands. Such programs do, however, require strict application of the principles of treatment and management if the land resource is to be maintained without impairment and deterioration.

RANGELAND VERSUS PASTURE

From the standpoint of development, treatment, use, and management, there is a distinction between rangeland and pasture, although both produce forage to be harvested by grazing animals. Rangeland is categorically in larger areas or grazing units than pasture. It is a primary component of a ranching operation, whereas a pasture is that of a farming operation and is usually comparatively small.

Rangeland is managed, maintained, or improved by the manipulation and management of the animals that graze on it. These same principles and techniques are applied to pastures, but more intensively than to rangelands. In addition, pastures are maintained or improved by cultural practices such as seeding, fertilizing, cultivation, or renovation, and possibly irrigation.

WHAT IS RANGE MANAGEMENT?

Range management is the practical application of a science dealing with the vegetation that is suitable and compatible with the environment that characterizes a given kind of rangeland. It takes into consideration the kinds of plants that will grow on a range for the productive use of both domestic livestock and adapted game animals. It also recognizes those plants that have little or no productive value to domestic livestock and may have little or no grazing value for game animals.

Range management deals specifically with the compatibility of plants and the ways they grow together in a balanced mixture on a kind of rangeland. How plants compete with one another, and how they react to degrees of grazing under variations of climate, are also important to range management. Which plants are grazed, and when, by the kind of animals using the range is the crux of good range management and livestock production.

READING THE LANDSCAPE

A first requirement of the range manager is to have the ability to read the landscape (range). He must be able to discern what he is looking at in terms of the various components in the range's present condition. And he must be able to interpret what he has observed in terms of the range resource. Such an interpretation would take into consideration the kinds and abundance of plants, the health and vigor of those plants, the kind and condition of soil, and the grazing use being made of the range. In addition, a judgment should be made as to the present production of the range in relation to its potential. To complete a reliable inventory of the range resources, needed changes for improving the range, and treatment and management to bring about such changes, must be considered.

Too often it is felt that the knowledge, training, and skill of a technically trained person are necessary for such interpretations. However, after a reasonable period of local adaptation, the ability to make such interpretations is the minimum requirement of any person engaged in range management. Time and experience have proved that alert and interested ranchers, laymen of various vocations, and professional people in allied fields can master the art of interpreting the resources of a range to a satisfactory degree.

BASIC PRINCIPLES OF RANGE MANAGEMENT

Under any set of conditions for rangeland, the basic objective is to harvest through livestock the highest possible yield of the highest quality of range forage on a sustained basis. That is, to do whatever is necessary to cause the best plants on a range to produce their highest yield, year in and year out. It takes pounds of grass to produce pounds of beef, wool, or mohair.

Grass is a living thing, depending on food, water, air, light, a place to grow, and plenty of room for a good root system, stems, leaves, flowers and seed. Like an animal or a human being, a plant's growth requirements must be satisfied if it is to survive, be healthy, and be productive. Never has it been possible to starve a profit out of an animal. Neither is it possible to starve production out of a plant. (The details of a plant's minimum growth requirements are discussed in Chapter 3, "Plant Growth and Response to Grazing").

It is not possible to achieve one-hundred per cent efficiency in satisfying growth requirements for all range plants growing together. Range plants are ordinarily found growing in a complex mixture where there is competition for all their required elements. This characteristic alone favors the most sturdy species; those with deeper and stronger root systems; those that dominate the space above ground by monopolizing sunlight, air, and room; those that are evaded by grazing animals.

These problems are magnified when the only tool for regulating plant growth requirements is the manipulation of grazing animals, and they are even more significant when grazing units are fenced into smaller areas. Before the advent of the barbed wire fence, animals moved over the range in search of fresh grass or seasonally palatable forage to such an extent that plant growth requirements were not seriously impaired. But with confinement of animals, repeat coverage in the grazing pattern often is a day-to-day activity.

When the needs and growth requirements of the best plants on a range have been provided for, requirements of all other plants will also have been adequately provided for, since grazing animals normally select the most palatable and most nutritious plants. They will do this repeatedly, or at least as long as there is sufficient regrowth to provide a bite. Thus, the less palatable and less desirable plants are left undisturbed, or are grazed to a lesser degree than the choice plants.

Therefore, achieving maximum plant growth and production for highest sustained yields requires livestock handling such that the factors of plant growth will be interfered with to the least possible extent.

There are four basic principles of range and livestock management that are cardinal to good range forage production and a sound ranching operation, and they dictate the more intricate and specific requirements of range management: (1) The proper degree of grazing use of the range forage; (2) The proper season of grazing according to the stage of plant development and selection of plants by the animals that graze the range; (3) The proper kind and class of livestock to make most efficient use of the range forage and to conform to other livestock adaptation factors, such as rough topography, sandy soils, sparse vegetation, or a predominance of grazable browse plants; (4) The proper distribution of grazing over all the range and of all desirable forage plants.

Each of these basic principles of range management are discussed as separate chapters. Their significance to the practical application of ways and means to achieve proper management of the range justifies their full consideration.

GRAZING MANAGEMENT INFLUENCES

There are many factors that directly influence the grazing patterns of both domestic livestock and game animals. Some of the most important are: location of water and other points of concentration in a pasture; distance from water to all accessible grazing areas; size and shape of pasture; climatic influences as wind direction and prevailing storms; kind of livestock; kind of vegetation areas; the number of animals in a grazing unit or pasture.

Since these factors deal primarily with livestock management and the ranch layout they are discussed in Chapter 14, "Livestock, The Tool in Range Management."

Chapter 2

KINDS OF RANGELAND

Kinds of rangeland as influenced by environment. A broad classification of these lands for the United States. The rangeland concept expanded in the United States to include southern and eastern lands. Some forest and depleted croplands converted to range use, and the significance of dual use of other lands. Regional classification of rangelands as influenced by environment. Influence of rainfall, temperature, humidity, light, soil, and topography on kinds and productivity of plants.

There are many kinds of rangeland distributed throughout the world, and the result is many different kinds of plants, communities of plants, plant associations, and plant compatibilities. Rangeland may vary widely from one continent to another, or between broad areas within a continent. And there are distinct differences in various land forms and the multiplicity of soils within rather restricted areas. Nonetheless, each type of rangeland is a product of the environment that prevails. The prevailing environment comprises the climate, the topography, and the soil. These factors, and their variations, are instrumental in establishing the many varied characteristics of a range, even within what might appear to be homogeneous conditions.

Thus, no two acres of rangeland are exactly alike, even though they may have the same general aspect. Like human beings, each parcel of rangeland has its individual characteristics. As any one or any combination of the factors of climate, topography, and soil change, the kind of range will change with it.

Since these differences are gradual and exhibit no real demarcation, there is a zone of transition from one kind of rangeland to another. That zone will contain plants and will have other characteristics of each of the zones on either side of it. This transition zone need not be disturbing, nor need it interfere with practical management of that range. In moving away from it into either of the adjacent zones, true characteristics will become more distinct until indicators of the other zone are no longer evident. An exception are plants or other distinguishing characteristics common to both zones. In such instances there would always be other prominent characteristics that do not occur in both zones, otherwise there would be no reason for the separation of the two zones. They would be one and the same.

An example of a transition zone from one kind of rangeland to another, wherein the overall aspect of both is generally the same, is the division between what is known as the true prairie and the mixed prairie. This division is due primarily to differences in rainfall and extends essentially from the Canadian border to the Gulf of Mexico. The line of demarcation coincides fairly closely to that separating zone 3 (Great Plains) from zone 4 (Subhumid Lands); see Fig. 1.

Generally speaking, this division separates rangelands that grow predominately tall grasses (zone 4), from rangelands that grow predominately a mixture of tall, mid-height, and short grasses (zone 3). Actually, throughout both of these zones may be found essentially all grasses common to either. However, with decreasing rainfall to the west, the grasses that dominate in the areas of higher rainfall (zone 4) become less abundant.

CLASSIFYING RANGELAND

In classifying rangeland, it is necessary to recognize differences due to pronounced variations in rainfall, since rainfall, as well as temperature, topography, and soil, determines the kinds of plants that will grow. Thus, rangelands are classed as arid, semi-arid, subhumid, and humid.

The Continental United States exhibits this classification distinctly. The pattern of rainfall extends from the summer dry climate of the Pacific coast, eastward through the arid region, the semi-arid or Great Plains region, the subhumid lands, and the humid east. These zones have been defined in the 1941 *Yearbook of Agriculture, Climate and Man,* by John Leighly, Reed W. Bailey, C. Warren Thornthwaite, Glenn T. Trewartha, and Carl O. Sauer (see also Figs. 2, 3, 4, and 5).

Each zone is quite distinct because of the type of characterizing vegetation, which may be briefly described as follows:

Cool season, annual grasses on noncrop and nonforest lands of the western fringe of the United States.

Fig. 1. A "broad classification" of rangelands of the United States. Differences in these zones can be attributed largely to climate, with soil and topography having their related influence. (From 1941 Yearbook of Agriculture, "Climate and Man.")

Zone 1. Summer Dry Climate (defined by John Leighly)
Zone 2. Arid Region (defined by Reed W. Bailey)
Zone 3. Great Plains (defined by C. Warren Thornthwaite)
Zone 4. Subhumid Lands (defined by Glenn T. Trewartha)
Zone 5. Humid East (defined by Carl O. Sauer)

Plants with low to moderate water requirements, producing sparse to moderate stands of grazable forage in the arid region.

Short and mid-height grasses, usually as prairies free of woody plants, common to the Great Plains.

Tall grass prairies, interspersed with wooded stream courses and some wooded areas of deciduous trees less than forest proportions, of the subhumid lands.

Forested lands, interspersed with tall-grass open prairies and meadows of the humid east.

Fig. 2. Mountains and ridges of the Southwest arid region. The grasses are threeawn, red grama, and chino grama. Lecheguillo, creosote bush, tasajillo, ocotillo, and Spanish dagger are the dominant plants on ridge in foreground.

Fig. 3. Semi-arid range of the Great Plains region. Blue grama and sideoats grama are the important grasses. Yucca and broom snakeweed are the most troublesome perennial invaders on this sandy loam site.

Fig. 4. Ranges of the subhumid region support grasses of the mixed prairie, including sideoats and blue grama, little bluestem, plains bristlegrass, Arizona cottontop, and buffalograss. Mesquite invasion is a serious problem on the southern ranges of this region.

Fig. 5. Open forest range of the humid east region. Brome and fescue grasses are important, as are tall bluestems, Indiangrass, and switchgrass. Grazable forage is confined mostly to open area.

VEGETATION TYPE CLASSIFICATION

The interactions of all environmental factors throughout the country have resulted in a wide range of active vegetation patterns. When not destroyed by man in the interest of more intensive land use, nature strives to maintain this original balance of plants and climate along with multiple life forms that are adapted to the habitat that prevails. Such an association is known as an ecological balance.

Even with interference by abuse and deterioration of such a balance, the resulting habitat will not be too greatly changed, owing to the controlling environment. However, such changes may cause a distinctly different aspect as reflected by the kind of vegetation resulting from such abuse and deterioration. For example, an area that originally was on open grassland prairie may eventually revert to a brush vegetation aspect. Although this has occurred over vast areas of rangeland, even though a different kind of vegetation dominates, it is there because it has adapted to the prevailing environmental conditions. Furthermore, plants that are not adapted will not become a component of the vegetation pattern for that area. This is true for areas of rather broad expanse, even though localized factors can and do reflect their influence to modify the environment, often resulting in a completely "out of place" vegetation pattern.

In recognition of these rather distinct areas of ecological environment and balance of nature, W. R. Chapline and C. K. Cooperrider, of the U.S. Forest Service, in their contribution to the 1941 *Yearbook of Agriculture*,[1] identify these areas of rangeland as: tall-grass prairie, short-grass plains, semi-desert-grass plains, Pacific bunchgrass prairie, shrub-grass ranges, sagebrush-grass range, salt-desert shrub, other shrub-grass ranges, timbered areas, woodlands, and open forests. E. J. Woolfolk, D. F. Costello, and B. W. Allred, in their contribution to the 1948 *Yearbook of Agriculture*,[2] recorded and described essentially these same kinds of rangeland for the United States, but in addition described areas of pinyon-juniper, woodland-chaparral, and coastal prairie. They also recognized as separate kinds of range, open forests of the west and southern forest ranges (Figs. 6, 7, 8, 9, and 10).

[1] W. R. Chapline and C. K. Cooperrider, *Climate and Man*, U.S. Forest Service, *Yearbook of Agriculture*, 1941.

[2] E. J. Woolfolk, D. F. Costello, and B. W. Allred, *Grass, Yearbook of Agriculture*, 1948.

Fig. 6. Pinyon-juniper range common to the southwest and inter-mountain states. Grasses adapted to a particular ecological zone dominate open areas when the range is in high condition.

Fig. 7. Open forest at the 9,000-foot elevation of the Rocky Mountains makes excellent summer range. Here, butterweed, cow parsnip, wild celery, columbine, and bearded wheatgrass provide good range, especially for sheep. (Photo courtesy U.S. Soil Conservation Service, Colorado.)

Fig. 8. Southern open forest range, where oak-hickory is the dominant tree growth. Big and little bluestem, Indiangrass, bearded panicum, a tall tridens, along with several low panicums and legumes, provide excellent range forage. (Photo courtesy U.S. Soil Conservation Service, Texas.)

Utilizing these classifications, almost any area in the United States, when used as rangeland, can be placed in one or another of the recognized ecological areas. This is, of course, significant from the broad aspect of kinds of ranching operations, intensity of management necessary, personal choice of where one prefers to enter the ranching business, and possibly other factors. However, from the standpoint of details of operation and practical management of rangeland, it is necessary to know more intimately the resources, environmental influences, and results of the individual ranching operation. These details are presented in subsequent chapters.

Fig. 9. Woodland-chaparral ranges are most common on the Pacific slope, but are found on other western ranges. Scrub oak, manzanita, coanothus, and mountain mahogany are common species of this type of range, which is generally steep and rough. Scrub oak and mountain mahogany are increasing on this northwest Texas range. (Photo courtesy U.S. Soil Conservation Service, Texas.)

RANGELAND CONCEPT EXPANDED IN THE UNITED STATES

In the past, rangelands of the United States were confined to the seventeen western states. Grazing lands of the eastern half of the country were identified, treated, and managed as pastureland, and were generally referred to as tame pasture. This area was further divided into the southern type and northern type, a division based primarily on introduced pasture grasses. Those adapted to the area south of an east-west line along the north boundaries of Arkansas, Tennessee, and North Carolina are the southern type, and introduc-

Fig. 10. Coastal prairie ranges are found in the Gulf States of the south. They may extend inland for a hundred or more miles with a flat, near sea-level topography. Grasses that tolerate marshlike conditions are important on these ranges. (Photo courtesy U.S. Soil Conservation Service, Louisiana.)

tions adapted north of that line characterize the northern type.

With increased knowledge and understanding of the value, treatment, and management of all native grasses grown under any set of environmental conditions, new concepts of grazing in the eastern half of the country have evolved. In the east are vast areas of open lands, once cropped but no longer suited for cultivation, being converted to grazing use. Cutover timber lands are being treated and managed as grazing lands. Wooded lands and certain forested areas, properly managed, are providing a grazing resource. Large areas of coastal marshlands of the southern states have become productive grazing areas.

In all these areas, the basic principles of range management are just as applicable as in the western range country where they have been developed.

INFLUENCE OF MOISTURE ON KINDS OF RANGELAND

Moisture and temperature are the two most significant environmental factors in determining the kinds of range plants that will grow. Of the two, moisture is of primary importance, but is so strongly influenced by temperature, the two can hardly be considered separately.

Water requirements determine the distribution of native plants into broad regions of adaptation. Water is also the limiting factor in the adaptation of plants in areas less than regional in size. It even determines variations in natural plant adaptation within rather restricted areas with only minor differences in such factors as soil and topography. Nevertheless, these differences and variations are influenced by temperature.

Moisture influences not only the kinds of plants found, but also their abundance and volume of production. This is most strikingly illustrated in the contrast between grass covered lands and lands producing woody plants or combinations of woody plants and grasses. These contrasting conditions generally are evidenced by differences in overall rainfall patterns from the dry southwest to the humid forested eastern areas.

As a general rule, moisture is the strongest influence on the kind of rangeland that will develop. Where there is a near continuous lack of moisture beyond the water requirements of most plants, a desert type of vegetation is formed. Where adequate moisture is available part of the year but insufficient during the remainder, grasslands usually develop. If there is a continuous supply of moisture, forests will result.

TEMPERATURE AND KINDS OF RANGELAND

Although moisture is the limiting factor in determining the kind of vegetation an area will support, temperature is the master regulatory factor of the environment. It involves both soil and air temperatures, each of which exerts a profound influence on the physiological activities of plants. Air temperature is the most reliable index to climate of any of the factors. It is the most easily measured, and maintains a relatively high degree of consistency over long periods of time. Although current local fluctuations may sometimes be great, the averages for periods of a year or longer seldom vary more than 10 to 15 per cent. Precipitation averages in the same locality may fluctuate as much as 80 to 90 per cent.

Air temperature affects all life processes of plants, therefore it is of great importance from the ecological and distribution standpoint. Within limits of plant reaction, temperature regulates the rate of photosynthesis or the process of plant food manufacture. Also, it regulates the rate of respiration and the rate of water loss or transpiration. Through these processes it strongly influences the life, growth form, and distribution of plants.

The beginning of growth within a given type of vegetation is controlled in large part by temperature, where other factors such as moisture are not limited beyond normal growth requirements. Also, the period of maximum growth of a community of plants usually corresponds with optimum temperatures for the kind of vegetation. This is generally true for either warm season or cool season plants.

Although average temperatures that prevail over the years govern the vegetation type within a given habitat, other factors, such as latitude, altitude, slope, exposure, prevalence of cloudy days, and wind movement, have significant local temperature effects on vegetation. Temperature decreases with an increase in latitude, owing to the change in angle of the sun's rays, and, consequently, the amount of radiant energy received at any one point. Although temperature varies inversely with altitude, there are exceptions where the valley is colder than adjacent higher elevations. This is a phenomenon known as temperature inversion, and it occurs usually at night and during cold winter months. It is a result of cold air flowing down from the higher elevations into the valley below, and being replaced by warmer air above.

Slope and exposure influence temperature through their effect upon the land exposed and the duration of and intensity of sunlight. Due to the angle of the sun's rays during the period of highest mean temperatures, which is summer, south and west exposures are hotter than north and east exposures. Cloudiness decreases sunlight intensity and thereby lowers temperature, while wind increases evaporation and generally has a cooling effect.

Owing to their physiological makeup, plants that are adapted to temperate or near-tropic climates have a much higher minimum degree of tolerance than plants adapted to colder habitats. Plants physiologically adapted to areas of much lower minimum temperatures do not require the higher temperatures of the more temperate climates for their growth activities. This does not mean that plants with the colder habitat limitations will not survive when moved to the warmer climate, but such a change will affect the normal growth cycle of such plants, particularly grasses.

Because of these temperature influences on plant reaction and response, distinct kinds of rangelands occur. Differences as to kinds of rangeland, due to these influences, are most significant in relation to distance from the equator. However, elevation and, to some degree, exposure to the sun's rays within a given longitudinal zone become significant.

HUMIDITY AND EVAPORATION

Humidity and evaporation may be considered minor factors of the climatic environment, yet they are important because of their effect on the physiological processes of plant growth. Humidity is the moisture that is in the air in the form of water vapor. Relative humidity is the amount or ratio of moisture in the air at any given time in relation to the amount there would be if the atmosphere were completely saturated.

Relative humidity is a significant factor of the climate in that it directly affects the rate of water loss through transpiration, and from the soil through evaporation. Here again, the amount of moisture in the atmosphere is regulated very largely by temperature. When other factors, such as wind currents, exposure, and elevation, remain relatively constant, the relative humidity will respond to temperature changes. A decrease in temperature results in an increase of the relative humidity, and an increase in temperature will cause a lower relative humidity, and consequently a higher evaporation rate. This factor alone can be very significant in the production of range forage, especially in areas of limited precipitation during the growing season.

Humidity and evaporation are also significant in determining kinds of range plants that will develop. From the equatorial zone of extreme high temperatures to a more polar zone, evaporation rates decrease very markedly, owing to lower temperatures that prevail over the growing season. This is not to say that extremely high temperatures never occur in areas far removed from the equator, but when they

Fig. 11. Coastal range under near tropical conditions. This type of range is developed under conditions of unlimited water, high temperatures, high relative humidity, and low evaporation and transpiration rates.

do, other factors prevail to at least partially compensate for excessive evaporation from the soil and transpiration from plants. It is generally recognized that in the Great Plains an annual precipitation of fourteen inches in the northern states is equivalent to eighteen inches in the southern states. This is true because of the relative humidity and evaporation control by lower temperatures to the north as compared to the south. These effects are also augmented by prevailing winds and their associated temperature. Wind movements, especially when temperatures are high, usually lower the humidity and increase evaporation, owing to the constant removal of the layer of moist air that tends to form near the ground surface as a result of soil evaporation and plant transpiration.

The significance of the relative humidity-temperature-evaporation phenomena is not restricted to areas of limited precipitation. In areas of unlimited soil moisture, the kind and amount of plants is limited by other environmental factors, such as room for growth, soil depth, fertility, topography, and, of course, maximum and minimum temperatures. Temperature control of humidity, and perhaps the resultant evaporation and transpiration rates, have a bearing on the kind of plants found.

Areas of the southeastern states, now recognized as range, support a kind of vegetation that borders on that of tropical climates. It is vegetation that thrives in an environment of unlimited water, smooth to rolling topography, productive soil, high temperatures, high relative humidity, and low evaporation and transpiration rates. These conditions vary little with changes in day and night temperatures, or from the beginning to the end of the growth period of the plant. Plants adapted to these conditions are affected very little by temperature changes of the surface atmosphere. The significant fact is that this environment results in a kind of vegetation or range peculiar to itself and which is confined to this particular area of environment (Fig. 11). Establishment, production, maintenance, and management of this type of rangeland requires somewhat different techniques than used in other areas, yet the basic fundamentals of plant growth and reproduction are essentially the same as for any other kind of rangeland.

LIGHT INFLUENCES THE KIND OF RANGELAND

Light and room to grow are basic requirements of any plant. Light, a result of sun rays, is all important in that only through the process of plant chlorophyll response to sunlight can soil minerals be converted into plant food. Therefore, without sun rays, plants have no source of a food supply to maintain their existence.

Some plants, such as those adapted to near tropic conditions, are less demanding in regard to light than many others. They have the ability to grow in close communion, with limited light and limited room. In contrast, plants that have become adapted to environments with other limited requirements, such as water or suitable temperatures, require more light, sun rays, and room for their existence. Plants in this category may be considered more rugged, but are usually less robust or even dwarfed in size. However, they very often have a characteristic of a higher and more prolonged nutritional quality than plants grown under less favorable conditions as to light, moisture, and room. This is a point in favor of range grasses common to the arid west, where growth requirements are limited.

TOPOGRAPHY AND KINDS OF RANGELAND

The North American continent, and especially the United States, is in a very favorable latitudinal position, that is, the distance from both the equator and the polar region. This location offers moderate climatic influences with respect to prevailing sunshine, air currents, and bodies of water. These factors maintain a reasonable degree of consistency as they prevail from west to east across the country between 30 and 50 degrees latitude. This distance, however, is sufficient to cause an average annual temperature of 70° F at approximately 30 degrees latitude and 35° F at approximately 50 degrees latitude. The differences are due primarily to the angle of occurrence and duration of the sun's rays.

If the land form or topography of the entire continent were uniform throughout, native vegetation, as well as cultivated crop production, would be correspondingly uniform. Changes would occur only as temperature, precipitation, and kinds of soil varied with distance from the equator. Fortunately, this phenomenon does not prevail, owing to the topographic relief of the country.

For the most part, three boundaries—west, south, and east—of the United States are adjacent to bodies of water and established sea level at their juncture (Fig. 12). From these points to the interior of the country are increased elevations and generally uneven, rolling to steeply rugged terrain. This does not imply that the entire land area of the United States is of irregular topography. There are vast areas, such as the Great Plains, that were, by processes of formation, made level and comparatively smooth (Figs. 13 and 14). Thus, the land pattern of the country comprises the level plain adjacent to the sea and level plains of much higher elevation, low rolling and hilly lands, and the extreme rough, broken, dissected, steep elevations to 16,000 feet and better. (Figs. 15 and 16). These factors of topography and elevation have a marked influence on the kinds of rangeland to be found. It is important to note, however, that these factors are closely related to all other factors of the environment in determining kinds of rangeland.

Fig. 12. A marsh range adjacent to the Gulf, supporting mostly plants that survive when partly submerged much of the year. Note the cattle walkways providing high ground for travel and for bedgrounds. (Photo courtesy U.S. Soil Conservation Service, Louisiana.)

Fig. 13. Semi-arid range of the southern Great Plains, with elevation 3,000 to 3,500 feet. Blue grama is the dominant grass.

Fig. 14. Rolling rangeland of the southern Great Plains near the
Canadian River. The elevation is approximately 4,000 feet. The
principal grasses are blue grama, sideoats grama, with lesser amounts
of silver bluestem and little bluestem. (Photo courtesy U.S. Soil Conservation Service, Texas.)

Fig. 15. Rolling hills and low mountains of the southern Rocky
Mountains, elevation 6,000 to 6,500 feet. Blue grama and sideoats
grama are the principal grasses, with oak and juniper timber in open
stands.

Fig. 16. Mountain and plateau ranges of Colorado at elevations of 10,000 feet and over are distinct as to the kind of vegetation produced. Slim stem muhly, pussy toes, fringed sage, showy cinquefoil, mountain avens, and Indian paintbrush are the principal plants of this range. (Photo courtesy U.S. Soil Conservation Service, Colorado.)

In general, there is a much wider variety of plants on an area of complex slopes, exposures, and elevations than on an area of uniform topography at any elevation. Therefore, topography as related to slope, exposure, and elevation has an important influence on the distribution, growth, and development of range plants in their various localized habitats.

As a rule, temperatures decrease and precipitation increases as the elevation increases. Also, evaporation decreases as the elevation increases. This is evidenced by a lack of tree growth, as well as other plants with relatively high water requirements, at elevations below 6,000 to 8,000 feet on mountainous areas of the southwest. As elevation increases above the approximate 6,000-foot level, a more favor-

Fig. 17. The north slope of a small hill in the southern Great Plains. The vegetation consists of little bluestem, sand bluestem, sideoats grama, blue grama, feather dalea, tall dalea, and a few palatable low-growing forbs.

able habitat occurs in regard to both moisture and temperature. Here, plants with higher water requirements, such as conifers, tall grasses, and even succulent type plants, are found in an otherwise arid or semi-arid climate.

In recognition of the kinds of rangeland as influenced by elevation and topography, as the distance from the equator becomes progressively greater, irrespective of localized topography and elevation, the kind of vegetation will correspond to the habitat that prevails. Such a habitat in the polar region at near sea level may be the same as that of a 15,000-foot elevation in a mountainous area of Colorado that is not more than 35 to 40 degrees latitude removed from the equator. Both these situations may reflect an above timberline type of vegetation. This is to say that an analysis of climatic

Fig. 18. South slope of the same hill shown in Fig. 17, with less than a quarter mile from one view to the other. Vegetation here includes black and blue grama, sideoats grama, threeawn, an occasional little bluestem, mesquite, yucca, and broom snakeweed. This community of plants requires a less favorable soil-water-plant relationship than those on the north slope.

conditions would show these habitats to be essentially the same for plant growth in each of the two locations.

Slope exposure is also a significant topographic factor that influences vegetation and the kind of rangeland. South and west slopes are warmer and drier than north and east slopes. Examples of this condition are perhaps more in evidence in areas where moisture for plant growth is somewhat limited, as in the arid southwest and Great Plains regions.

In the mountainous areas of the southwest, there are thrifty growths of coniferous trees on the north and east slopes, whereas such trees are poorly developed or entirely lacking on south and west slopes. In the Great Plains, on rolling to hilly ranges with significant slopes, usually along stream courses, good stands of mid and tall grasses of the subhumid region dominate north and east slopes. In contrast, sparse to moderate stands of short grasses are dominant on south and west slopes (Figs. 17 and 18).

These conditions prevail for several very logical reasons. South slopes in particular, and west slopes to a greater degree than north and east slopes, are more nearly perpendicular to the sun's rays. Likewise, they are exposed to sunlight for a longer period of time than are north and east slopes. West slopes are exposed to direct sun rays in the afternoon, when atmospheric temperatures are highest. These conditions affect both the temperature of the atmosphere and soil air. This, in turn, causes an increased rate of evaporation and less soil moisture for plant growth and development. Thus, different kinds of rangeland occur in a localized broken terrain country, often requiring different treatment and management to maintain them in their highest state of production.

SOIL INFLUENCES THE KIND OF RANGELAND

Soil is a basic resource and the foundation of the range environment. It may be considered as the storehouse of the effects of the combined environmental factors that prevail. All elements of climate and all variations of topography exert their characteristic influences in direct relationship to the soil at any given location, and thus a kind of rangeland is developed.

Soil formation and development is dependent upon the factors of time, the substratum of material from which it is derived, the presence or absence of a vegetation cover, the climate, and the stability or erosion factor. Without going into the chemical process involved in the formation of the substance of a soil, it should suffice to say that soil is composed of both mineral and organic materials, including water (hydrogen and oxygen), carbon dioxide, nitrogen, phosphorus, potassium, sulfur, calcium, iron, and magnesium. Other mineral elements that are important when in compounds, and which are generally recognized as trace elements, include boron, manganese, iodine, fluorine, copper, aluminum, sodium, silicon, and chlorine. In addition to these mineral materials is the important organic substance resulting from the decay of plant and animal life, including minute organisms of the soil mass. A soil containing these substances in balanced proportions is classified as a mature, mineralized soil.

Under prevailing conditions of soil formation, when completely saturated, it contains 20 to 30 per cent water, 1 to 5 per cent organic matter, and 65 to 80 per cent mineral matter.

Temperature, in association with soil water, regulates the rate of solubility and reaction of the mineral elements of a soil. It also affects the reaction of organic substances in the soil.

Whether a soil is used for range, crop production, forest, or any other purpose, the way the elements occur together is of great importance. This is referred to as soil texture and soil structure, and it regulates in large part the reaction and response to other factors of the environment and subsequent plant growth and development.

Soil texture and structure can provide compensating benefits that in turn influence the distribution of important grass species, especially some tall grasses. Big bluestem, switchgrass, and Indiangrass, are important grasses of the subhumid or true prairie of the United States. This area is generally regarded as a deep, fine-textured, productive soil. Also, the true prairie is in the medium- to high-rainfall belt. Thus, a deep, fertile soil with high water holding capacity is characterized by an abundance of those species in the climax of the true prairie. To the west, however, including the Great Plains, and to a degree the arid region of the southwest, soils similar to those of the true prairie will not support tall grasses, owing to insufficient available moisture. Since the normal rainfall is much less than that of the true prairie, and since there is a limited amount of water available to be retained by those fine-textured soils to the west, there simply is not enough available moisture to support tall grasses. On the other hand, such tall grasses are important climax species on deep sandy soils of these more arid regions, because the texture and structure of those sands permit rapid and deep penetration of all rainfall, including light showers. Even though the water holding capacity of these soils is comparatively low, the deep penetration and below-normal evaporation resulting from the thick layer of surface sand insure an adequate amount of moisture for these tall grasses.

From the point of view of range management and livestock production, the interactions of soil, climate (temperature and precipitation), and topography result in a kind of rangeland. To the extent that these interactions result in the production of a reasonably uniform community of plants, that area is identified as a specific kind of rangeland. For convenience and clearness of identity, such an area is commonly referred to as a range site.

Kinds of rangeland may be identified as rather large areas supporting a rather uniform kind of vegetation. Examples of such areas would be valleys, areas along stream courses, shallow ridges, or even areas of considerable expanse, such as flat lands of the Great Plains. Though such an identification and classification may work for practical management purposes, there may be drastic differences within these areas, both as to kinds and amounts of plants. This would be a result of the kind of soil and its relationship to climate and possibly topography. Thus, both management and production would be affected. As a general rule, soil texture and soil depth will be the basic differences that occur. The example of tall grasses being adapted to sandy soils in the mixed prairie and heavy soils in the true prairie, as described above, illustrates this point as applied to broad areas such as a vegetation zone. But perhaps more important is the response to different kinds of plants within rather homogeneous areas because of salient differences in soil. A valley within a single plant and climate zone may have both coarse textured and fine textured soils. Each would produce entirely different kinds of plants. Thus, each would be a different kind of rangeland.

Plant response on these different kinds of soil is dependent on the soil-water-plant relationship. That relationship includes the ability of the soil to take water and its capacity to hold it for plant use. The kind of plant response is a direct factor of the amount of water available through the growth cycle over a period of years. This response is, of course, regulated by the fertility holding capacity of that soil, as indicated by the depth, texture, and structure.

The native vegetation produced is a direct response to any soil and its environment. The vegetation on a single kind of soil will be reasonably consistent, regardless of the treatment given the plants that grow there. With adverse conditions, the vegetation will decline in a fairly uniform pattern on that soil. As conditions improve, it will move rather consistently toward a climax vegetation. This same plant response does not prevail on a different kind of soil, but the response of a different group of plants, suited to the different soil, will also be consistent.

These characteristics and interactions between a kind of soil and the plants it will support identify a range site and resultant range conditions. Such parcels of land are very significant as a basis for managing grazing resources.

Chapter 3

PLANT GROWTH AND RESPONSE TO GRAZING

A practical interpretation of the process of plant growth. How grazing management can be used to insure essential requirements for plant growth. Importance of plant structure and development in grazing management. The relationship of seasonal climatic influences on plants and their reaction to grazing. The importance of maintaining range plants in a strong and healthy condition for efficient forage production.

With modern scientific progress, knowledge of parts and functions of the human body is becoming more commonplace. The medical doctor is becoming more skilled in interpreting this knowledge and conveying information to the layman. The plant scientist has gained knowledge and an understanding of vegetation which also is basic to human life, and such knowledge must be understandable to the manager of rangelands if he is to maintain, improve, and bring into production those lands.

Range plants are living individuals, rather complex in construction, but designed to function with precision. How they respond, not only to their environment, but to the treatment and use given them, is the basis for effective and practical range management techniques and practices.

To the layman, the essential parts of a plant include leaves, stems, roots, buds, flower, and fruit. These are, of course, the end products of a plant development. The plant scientist recognizes such parts as culm, ligule, node, internode, inflorescence, stamen, anther, pistil, merestimatic tissue, chlorophyll, chromosomes, genus, and species. To be effective in the management of range plants, the rancher must also be familiar with these parts and the ways in which they function in the processes of plant growth. He must also know how plants relate to soil, climate, treatment, and use by grazing animals. All plants are basically the same in regard to characteristics of structure and their growth requirements. However, plants that are common to the range country are unique in their ability to resist abuse, to respond to treatment and management, and to perpetuate in the environment to which they are adapted.

HOW PLANTS GROW[1]

Soil is the home of plants, and the characteristics of soil influence the kind of plants that will grow in a particular area. But more significantly, the kind of soil influences plant development in regard to stature and quality. A soil with a capacity to take in and hold good amounts of water and fertility elements is a productive soil, and plants growing in it are productive plants. Therefore, soil and climate dictate the kind of range and its limitations of production.

Plant growth and development are dependent on four essentials: (1) a strong root system that extends throughout the soil profile allotted to that plant; (2) a normally developed and maintained top growth or vegetative production; (3) an adequate amount of space, both below and above the soil surface; and (4) an adequate supply of plant food materials, including water.[2] These are the minimum requirements for maximum growth and production of any plant, whether it be for forage, fruit, flower, tuber, or wood products.

It is commonly believed that a soil well supplied with the mineral elements used for plant food, or "fertilizer" when applied artificially, is insurance of high production. This is not necessarily true, because of the way in which plants function is seeking their growth requirements. The root system, in addition to being the means of anchoring the plant to the soil, is the gathering mechanism of plant food materials. These materials, of which nitrogen, phosphorus, potash, iron, manganese, magnesium, boron, sulphur, and several others, are important, are found in varying amounts in a fertile soil. Through chemical reactions, biological actions, and to a degree physical influences, these elements become soluble, usually a little at a time, but as a continuing process. Thus, water becomes the carrying agent of plant food materials.

[1] H. L. Leithead, *Grass, How It Grows* (USDA Soil Conservation Service, Fort Worth, Texas, 1966).

[2] B. W. Allred, *Practical Grassland Management*, 1950.

The soil solution, charged with the various elements that are available, is taken into the plant roots and transported upward and into the vegetative parts, stems, and leaves. Within the fleshy part of the leaf is the green substance called chlorophyll ("leaf green"). Over the surface of the leaf, small openings, stomata, take from the atmosphere carbon dioxide, a gas. Inside the leaf are formed the raw materials for plant food.

Without sun rays upon the leaves and green stems of the plant, little or no further action would take place. But by absorption of some of the energy from the sun's rays, the chlorophyll breaks down the compounds of water and carbon dioxide, changing them to carbon, hydrogen, and oxygen. These materials again unite into new compounds which, by further actions and reactions, are converted to sugars and starches. During this process, excess oxygen is transpired from the leaf surface into the atmosphere as free oxygen, an important source in maintaining the oxygen supply necessary to all forms of life, including man.

This series of reactions within green plants, under the influence of sunlight, manufactures food necessary to plant life and growth. The process is known as photosynthesis (literally, "putting together by means of light"). It implies two basic requirements of the plant. There must be an adequate root system to gather and transport the raw material for plant food; and there must be adequate green leaf and stem surface in which the process of plant food manufacture can take place. A deficiency in either of these areas limits the food supply for maximum plant production.

After the food supply has been manufactured, it is translocated back down to the roots and lower stems of the plant. In grasses, this area is commonly called the crown of the plant. Plants other than grasses are equipped with fleshy or woody roots in which food reserves are stored. A stored food supply is necessary if the plant is to develop new cells and tissues that reflect plant growth. During the active growth period of a plant, the food manufacturing process, which includes translocation, storage, and redistribution throughout the plant, is a continuous process. However, once the plant ceases to be active or becomes dormant for any reason, and the food manufacturing process is interrupted, the food storage supply becomes a very important factor in the regrowth and future production and maintenance of the plant.

The growth processes of plants are regulated strongly by seasons or temperature changes. These changes, in conjunction with such influences as moisture, plant nutrients, hormones, and enzymes, determine the life cycle of plants, both annual and perennial. Thus, temperature, the regulatory factor of plant growth, is important to range plant production and management. Changes in plant activity essentially reverse themselves with distinct changes of temperature, from dominating cool to warm, and warm to cool, according to seasons of the year.

The fact that a solute moves from a cool to a warm environment is significant to plant growth. It is important from the standpoint of seed germination, as well as activation of plant dormancy, in the case of perennials. During the season when plants are growing, both atmospheric and soil temperatures are nearly the same. Coincident with seasonal changes of climate is the cooling effect of atmospheric temperatures and reactions of growth substances within the plants. These combined influences have an effect on plant growth. Active growth ceases and the process of plant maturity takes place. If the plant is an annual, seed will mature, and the remains of the plant will progressively disintegrate. With perennial plants, seed maturity takes place, but death of the plant is not likely. However, all perennial plants, except those with woody structure, disintegrate (as do annuals) but usually more slowly. But during the maturing process of perennials, processed food within the plant is translocated and stored in underground stems and roots.

During the dormant period, atmospheric and soil temperatures again tend to equalize. However, they are below what is suitable for most plant growth activity. Nevertheless, some root growth takes place during the dormant period.

With higher atmospheric temperatures, again a result of seasonal climatic changes, soil temperatures gradually increase to correspond to that of the atmosphere. This temperature change, along with growth stimulants within the plant, again activate plants into growth and production. Thus the cycle of perennial plant growth is complete, going from active growth to dormancy and back to active growth. In lay terminology, these changes coincide with the sap's rising in the spring and its going down in the fall.

Most plants, and notably those that provide range forage, respond to, and, in fact, require these alternate growth and rest periods for their normal and highest production. There are exceptions among plants that are adapted to a climate that is continuously warm enough to maintain uniform atmospheric and soil temperatures—near-tropical conditions

From the standpoint of range management, seasonal climatic changes that result in alternate periods of active growth and dormancy are important for both warm season and cool season plants. The plants that actively grow during the warm season are dormant during the cool season, and those that maintain active growth during the cool season become dormant during the warm season. These facts need to be taken into account in grazing use and management of plants with these different growth characteristics. Too often, effort is made to keep cool season plants active and usable during the warm season, which usually results in abusive use of those plants. And warm season plants that retain a reasonably high protein content during their dormant period are too often grazed without regard for plant requirements during that period. Roots continue to develop and grow during dormancy, replacing those that become inactive and die off. Also there continues to be some activity of translocation of proteins and sugars from the apparent dormant vegetative parts of the plant.

How serious is close grazing of range forage during the winter or dormant period? Obviously, such use is not as damaging as it would be during the growth period, when the food manufacturing parts, leaves, and stems, would be destroyed. However, damage is done in that all remaining plant food materials are removed. Plant crowns, in which are located buds for next season's growth, reserve food supplies, and surface feeder roots are left unprotected from the ravages of the weather and the trampling of livestock. Although these factors may seem insignificant, they do have an effect on range plants. If permitted to repeat over a period of years, the combined results can cause serious deterioration of the range.

PROVIDING PLANT GROWTH REQUIREMENTS
THROUGH GRAZING MANAGEMENT

Good grazing management, proper range use, and maximum production can be achieved by adhering to a few simple rules relative to plant growth and development: (1) Never use more than approximately fifty per cent of the current year's production of important range forage plants. (2) Allow new plant growth to get beyond infancy and ahead of the livestock by not grazing too early. (3) Graze during the best season of use for both the plant and the livestock.

(4) Graze with the kind of livestock that will make most efficient use of the forage with least abuse to individual plants, or to the plant community.

These rules are followed to one degree or another on most successful ranching operations. Perhaps they are achieved most satisfactorily by the use of commonly accepted grazing management practices. Proper range use, deferred grazing, rotation grazing, or even year long or season long use of properly stocked ranges are good management practices. A working knowledge of how plants react to degrees of grazing, drought periods, or other stresses and adversities is most helpful in planning management commensurate with plant requirements to insure the desired results.

Forage production from range grasses is primarily the stems and leaves of the plant. That is what the manager sees and measures as his forage crop, and recognizes as the essential basic resource of his ranching operation. Although forage is important as the product of the range crop, the purpose and function of the roots and fruit or seed crop cannot be overlooked.[3]

The root system is the foundation of the individual plant, the plant community, and the range. Without a strong, well developed root system, maximum production is impossible, regardless of fertility of the land, climatic conditions, and the best management. Also of significance to the production and maintenance of grass is the seed crop, even though it is not a measure of forage production. Seed maturity from good, healthy grass plants does provide for the establishment of new plants, as long as there is room and a need for them. But more important, a good, productive seed crop is indicative of a healthy stand of grass and is a progressive step toward maintenance and improvement. Strong plants, as evidenced by a good seed crop, mean there is a strong root system. These characteristics of growth are more important in maintaining a stand than benefits that might result from the seed crop for reproduction.

Inasmuch as conditions of range deterioration prevail over most of the range country, it behooves the range manager to keep the best kinds of plants his range will produce. Regardless of how depleted the range might be, some of the better kinds of plants remaining should provide the key to the management needed to improve that range.

[3] J. E. Weaver, "Underground Plant Development in Its Relation to Grazing," *Ecology*, 11:543–557.

Where this is not true, the alternatives are to use and manage what is there for highest production and maintenance, or undertake to reestablish a stand of more desirable grasses by range seeding.

Much has been written, said, and recommended about proper range use. "Take half and leave half the forage." "It takes grass to grow grass." "Defer the range." These are but three of the many generalized concepts for the range manager to follow. Each of these concepts are good and will invariably be of some benefit to the range. However, a simple understanding of how plants respond to their environment and the treatment and use made of them should explain the "why," and possibly the "how" and "when" of these concepts.

THE PLACE AND FUNCTION OF GRASS STEMS

From the practical standpoint, the stem of the grass plant may be considered the working tool for good management. The stem is made up of nodes, or joints, and the internode, or the part of the stem between the nodes. It also has a sheath, or cover, that emerges from a growth bud at the node. The sheath usually covers the span of one internode but may extend farther up the stem proper. These various parts, along with the seed that is produced as the plant reaches maturity, constitutes the foliage or forage crop that is produced from range grasses. Of course, many other plants are also important to the range.

Of equal importance for management and production of grass is that part of the stem that is not seen and seldom considered. It is the lower or base end of each stem that is embedded in the crown or stool of the plant.[4] Sod forming grasses such as bermudagrass, buffalograss, and curley mesquitegrass, do not form a distinct crown or stool, yet they too have a basal part of the stem that functions as if in a crown.

This underground stem is of the same general construction as the stem above ground, but greatly modified. It too is made up of nodes and internodes that are distinct, even though compressed into a length that may vary from $\frac{1}{2}$-inch to 2 inches (Fig. 19), depending on the species. The grama grasses, short threeawns, and other short grasses

4 C. A. Rechenthin, *Elementary Morphology of Grass Growth and How It Affects Utilization* (USDA Soil Conservation Service, 1956).

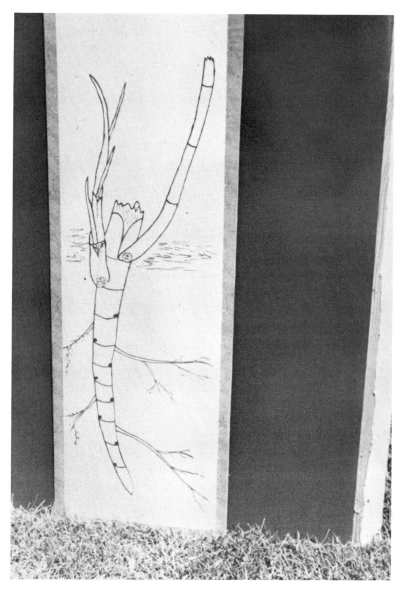

Fig. 19. Enlarged drawing of underground stem of blue grama. Note the bud formation at each node. The top bud, first to activate and emerge, has been nipped off, and there has been subsequent emergence from the second bud.

may have an underground stem ½-inch to ¾-inch long. Mid-height grasses, such as little bluestem, sprangletop, and some dropseeds develop underground stems of 1- to 1½-inches long. Longer underground stems are found in the crowns of tall-growing grasses, such as big and sand bluestem, switchgrass, Indiangrass, and the tall, robust dropseeds.

Within these lengths are varying numbers of nodes and internodes, and the internodes will vary with the kind of grass. Contrary to what might seem most logical, the greater numbers often occur on the shorter underground stem segments. For example, blue grama, which usually is not more than ½- to ¾-inch in length, may have twelve to fifteen distinct nodes, very much compressed, with essentially no visible internode. On the other hand, switchgrass, Indiangrass, and other tall grasses that may have an underground stem segment of 1½ inches or more, may develop only three to five nodes, but with correspondingly longer internodes.

What is the significance of these variations in different kinds of grasses? Each node on the underground stem is a point of origin for new stem growth. At each node is a potential growth bud. These are generally located on alternate sides of the stem, from the first or top node down to the lower or tip end. Warm season grasses form these buds in the fall, provided the plant is functioning normally; that is, provided there is green leaf and stem growth in which plant food is manufactured, and provided plant food is translocated down into the crown or mass of underground stems in sufficient quantity to support bud formation. If this process is not permitted in the fall because of too close grazing, or does not occur for any reason, bud formation does not take place on schedule. This point alone is ample justification for seeing to it that the range is not too closely grazed in the fall of the year. When there is not enough food material for development of these buds in the fall, it becomes necessary for them to be formed the following spring before normal spring growth can take place. This means that spring growth will be delayed two weeks or more while bud formation is taking place. With this process, it becomes necessary to use stored plant food that is so vitally needed for support of the early growth until the green-leaf-plus-sunlight process begins to take place. Thus, spring growth of the grass crop is handicapped when, for any reason, normal fall processes do not take place. Also, because of these limitations on available plant food at the critical beginning of spring growth, the number of growth buds will be reduced accordingly.

WHEN PLANTS REVIVE FROM DORMANCY

When atmospheric temperatures are higher than soil temperatures in the spring, plants begin to activate. Roots begin to gather soil water that is charged with soluble plant food materials. This solute begins to move upward through the plant by root pressure and by cohesion. The solution transports sugars and starches to growth points of live tissue within the activated part of the plant. The underground stem buds are among the very first points to become activated and in need of plant food.

This growth process is most intricately developed to meet the needs of the plant in its struggle for existence and survival. Generally, the very top bud at the first underground node is the first to become active. It puts forth a tiny, sheath-enclosed shoot that emerges into the sunlight within a couple of days after breaking from the bud capsule. When all its growth requirements of food, water, room, and sunlight are available, and if there is no physical disturbance, that shoot will continue to develop until it reaches maturity, including flower and seed, if it is a seed producing stem.

This process takes place for every underground stem that is included in the crown of the plant, provided growth requirements are in sufficient abundance to support them. Furthermore, if the plant is healthy and vigorous, additional buds on each underground stem may develop, adding to the total number of stems and the volume of production of that plant. However, this additional bud development is dependent on available stored plant food or on newly manufactured plant food, as a result of the very earliest shoot growth and development.

PLANT REACTION TO GRAZING

When spring growth starts, it is most appetizing to livestock that have been on dry feed all winter. They start grazing the very first shoots that appear. This occurs earlier for small animals, such as sheep and goats, than for cattle and horses. If there are sufficient numbers of grazing animals to nip all grass shoots as soon as they are available, the grass will never get ahead of the grazing. Thus, the physiological reaction of grass plants to grazing becomes important to good range management.

Grass response to grazing of new shoots varies with different grasses.[5] Branson found that it depends on the location of the growth point of the stem relative to its exposure above ground. If that point is an inch or more above ground (protruding above the crown), it is very susceptible to being grazed. And once the growth point is grazed off, no new leaves will be produced by that stem bud.

This growth point of vegetative stems is significant in forage production, since these stems, rather than seed stems, produce the major portion of range forage.

Furthermore, once a stem enters the reproductive phase, no new leaves are produced. Therefore, seed stems once grazed cannot be relied on for additional forage production during that growth cycle of the plant. This simply means that close, early grazing may result in forage production being reduced to a small percent of the potential. Under such conditions, any regrowth from plants subjected to that intensity of grazing will have to come from new buds lower down on the underground stem, as shown in Fig. 19. Just how many of these new buds will activate will depend largely on stored food available and additional food manufactured by the plant. The latter source will be very limited, since few, if any, green leaves will be available for the manufacturing process to take place.

Not all range grasses are subject to the same response to early grazing, because they grow differently. Branson's work with eight commonly distributed range grasses indicates different heights to which the growth point in vegetative stems are elevated above ground level. Thus, there are corresponding differences in their resistance to grazing pressure. The growth point in relation to the soil level is described by Branson as follows:

"Switchgrass—by early June, well above minimum height cattle can graze."

"Western Wheatgrass—by June 9, the growing point elevated more than five inches."

"Big bluestem—below ground level until late July. Thereafter readily accessible and very palatable."

"Little bluestem—slightly more than an inch above ground."

[5] Farrel A. Branson, "Two New Factors Affecting Resistance To Grazing," *Journal of Range Management*, (Vol. 6, No. 3, May 1953).

"Kentucky bluegrass—below the surface throughout the growing season."

"Buffalograss—slightly above the ground, except for those that terminated in a stolon."

"Blue grama—at or near the ground surface throughout the growing season."

"Sideoats grama—near the surface of the soil throughout the growing season."

The above information clearly indicates how these grasses may be expected to respond to close grazing, especially early in the season. Switchgrass production can be greatly reduced by close grazing by early June, whereas big bluestem will not be seriously affected until late July. But thereafter, big bluestem is abusively grazed because of its palatability and nutritive quality. Western wheatgrass is very susceptible to abusive grazing throughout most of the grazing season. Being a cool season grass, it has a longer grazing season than warm season grasses, subjecting it to even greater abuse.

Theoretically, little bluestem is perhaps the least resistant to grazing pressure. However, according to Branson, the ratio of seed stems to vegetative stems may actually be a more significant factor than location of the growth point as the reason for a lack of resistance to grazing. And yet, the grazing pattern of little bluestem usually leaves an abundance of old stems affording protection from too close grazing. These facts no doubt contribute much to the fact that this grass appears to have resistance to grazing, up to a point. But when that point of heavy use is reached, destructive grazing occurs very rapidly.

The other four grasses—Kentucky bluegrass, buffalograss, blue grama, and sideoats grama—all have very favorable growthpoint positions, being at or below ground level throughout the growing season. This provides them with a built-in resistance to close grazing. And it is a highly significant factor contributing to the persistence of these grasses, even under abusive grazing.

There seems to be a direct correlation between grazing off the growing point and grass stand maintenance. Field experience bears out the fact that of the eight grasses in Branson's study, those with the growing point elevated above ground level decrease with heavy grazing. Those with the growing point at ground level normally increase in the stand at first. Then with continued pressure grazing, resulting in little or no photosynthetic processes, they too decrease. Plants with a preponderance of seed stems over vegetative stems usually decrease under heavy grazing. This is also due to a lack of photosynthetic processes.

The ratio of seed stems to vegetative stems is also important to grass response to grazing. As pointed out above, the fact that once a seed stem is grazed, no new leaves are produced, imposes a limit on production. This is true even with proper grazing during the growing season. This makes the ratio of seed stems to vegetative stems, especially early in the grazing season, an important factor in both management of grass and production. As a part of the work done by Branson on the growth point of grasses, he also determined stem ratios. For the various grasses the ratio of seed stems to vegetative stems was as follows:

Grass	Seed Stems	Vegetative Stems
Switchgrass	2.15	1.0
Western wheatgrass	1.0	16.3
Big bluestem	1.0	2.82
Little bluestem	3.2	1.0
Kentucky bluegrass	1.0	11.6
Buffalograss	1.0	6.84
Blue grama	1.0	6.49
Sideoats grama	1.0	2.09

The matter of seed stem ratio to vegetative stems influences grass production in several ways. A grass with a low seed stem to vegetative stem ratio, such as blue grama, has the potential of high production early in the growing season. The many vegetative stems, even though very short as compared to a seed stem, will produce an abundance of long, leafy foliage. As long as the growth point is not nipped off, even though the leaves are grazed, those leaves will continue to make regrowth if there is an available food supply. This process will continue throughout the growing season. There will also be new buds sending forth leaves if growing conditions are satisfactory.

It is from these vegetative stems that the greater portion of high-quality range forage is produced (Figs. 20 and 21). With good, healthy plants, most of this production is made in the first half of the growing season.

Fig. 20. Blue grama plants managed for maximum production. The first seed heads appeared June 23, 1970, on these two-year old plants.

A healthy stand of grass will continue this desirable productive growth of mostly foliage stems and leaves until about mid-way through the growing season for any particular area. In the southern plains, which extends roughly along an east-west line through Lubbock, Texas, and Roswell, New Mexico, the halfway date of the growing season is about June 25 to July 1 in a normal year. Farther north to about the Oklahoma Panhandle, a distance of 200 to 250 miles, this date is about July 3 to 8. Specific dates for other areas will, of course, correspond to the beginning and length of the growing season.

Following the near mid-point of the normal growth season of the healthy plant, hormones act on the growth buds of the underground stem, resulting in much of the growth energy going to fruiting stems. Thereafter, a majority of new stems will be seed producing, and the seed crop becomes evident within a few days. Under optimum conditions, once the seed production process starts, it develops rapidly. Most range grasses require only three to six days from the time a seed

Fig. 21. The yield from five plants shown in Fig. 20. A total of 6,250 pounds per acre, air dry, was the yield. This condition does not represent grazing conditions, but the first year (1969) crop was harvested to a degree well within the limits of proper use.

producing stem emerges into the sunlight until it reaches most of its height and flowering parts, or until the seed head forms. In fact, this rapid fruiting stem development will occur even when the health and vigor of the plant may be low. This is nature's way in the survival and reproduction of a species.

These being the normal growth processes by which maximum forage is produced, it is only logical that range management techniques should provide optimum growth conditions throughout the growing season, and especially during the early part of the season when the bulk of the range forage crop is produced.

This process of plant growth and reaction to heavy grazing in early spring may well reduce the current year's production of grass by as much as fifty percent or more. Furthermore, the fact that the livestock will very likely be ahead of the grass during the entire growing season will further deplete the range and the next year's production as well. The grass never has a chance to catch up with its normal pattern of growth. It continues to decline in vigor and decrease in size and content of the root system, as well as numbers of potential stems, and the result is an unhealthy condition of the range.

Response to grazing range plants other than grasses must also be considered in range management. Forbs, legumes, and browse plants all contribute to the forage production of the range where they occur. Their response to grazing differs somewhat from that of grass plants. The growth point of these plants is at the terminal end of branches and twigs. Once these terminal buds are nipped off, growth from that point ceases. Additional growth from that branch or twig must come from new growth buds formed back down the stem structure of the plant.

The volume of production from regrowth from non-grasslike plants may be considerably less than what might be expected from grass plants. The reason is that new buds on plants other than grasses are really secondary to the original plant structure. With grasses, buds for the purpose of regrowth are primary in the structure of the plant. They have only to be activated, and with adequate plant food will come forth with another stem equal to any other that may have preceded it in development.

It should be recognized, however, that secondary growth from any range plant will be regulated by the time factor for growth, development, and maturity. Coupled with the time factor would be other related growth factors, such as length of daylight hours, temperature, and plant food. When regrowth stimulus occurs late in the growth season, maturity of that new growth will be speeded up and production curtailed accordingly. Sometimes plants, including grasses, will seed with very little, if any, elongation of the seed stem or branch. This is characteristic when regrowth stimulus occurs late or near the normal fruiting period for that plant.

UNHEALTHY PLANTS AND UNFAVORABLE GROWING CONDITIONS

When less than optimum growth conditions prevail, grass plants respond accordingly. They may have been weakened by too close grazing over a period of years. The reserve food supply may be deficient for spring growth as a result of close grazing the previous fall. Drought conditions in the fall may have prevented the normal process of food manufacture by the action of sunlight on green leaves. Excessive competition from weeds, weedy grasses, or brush may have robbed forage plants of needed food materials and water. Or, too early and too heavy spring grazing may have prevented grass plants from functioning normally during the critical stages of growth.

When such conditions occur naturally, or are permitted by improper grazing management, plant reaction will be something less than normal, and decreased yields will result.

The law of nature for any form of life, plant or animal, is to perpetuate its kind. Thus, with range plants, the production of seed is of first importance, and vegetative or foliage production becomes secondary. Any grass plant that is weak and unthrifty will produce seed bearing stems from the beginning of growth in early spring at the expense of foliage production. For example, with blue grama, there will be a ratio of five or six to one seed stems over vegetative stems. Under these conditions, rapid growth and seed head formation occur with comparatively few leaves exceeding 2 or 3 inches in length. This is in comparison to 10- to 15-inch leaf length when growth conditions for production are optimum. Under such adverse conditions, the total volume of forage production will actually be reduced by 50 or possibly 75 per cent (Fig. 22). The same condition will prevail, regardless of the health and vigor of plants, when adequate moisture for normal spring beginning growth is delayed. The statement is often made by ranchers, especially in the southern and southwestern

Fig. 22. *Three blue grama plants grown under identical conditions, except management. Number 1 is approximately one-fifth of the total crown area of a well managed plant. Number 2 is the entire plant of a range that had complete rest during the entire growing season followed by six to seven months of heavy use. Number 3 is a complete plant from a range grazed indiscriminately with no limitations or restrictions on the degree of use.*

range country, that rain by the first of September will make grass for the winter. This is generally true, but the question is, "How much grass, and what management is required"?

Actual weight yields from good, thrifty stands of blue grama have been no more than 25 per cent of the potential yield due to spring and summer rains being delayed until well past the mid-point of the normal growing season. Here again, vegetative stem buds are converted to fruiting stem buds in an attempt for the species to perpetuate itself. It is not uncommon to note within ten days or two weeks a crop of seed heads waving in the breeze following late summer, drought-breaking rain. A logical interpretation is "plenty of grass."

These characteristics of plants and plant reactions simply mean that ranges not managed to insure maximum growth requirements possible for normal development and production will not yield their potential. A lack of the essential growth requirements may be due to natural causes or to mismanagement. They may be a result of seasonal or annual occurrences. Or, they may recur over a period of years. Nevertheless, they do need to be recognized and grazing use adjusted according to current conditions and production.

It is not always possible to follow a grazing management plan or to make needed adjustments in the plan to meet the needs of all kinds of plants on a range. However, almost without exception, there will be one or two forage plants on a range that are preference plants to the livestock. These may well serve as a barometer of use in determining when management adjustments are needed. Generally, when the needs of these plants are met, all other plants on that range will be adequately cared for. These preference plants will, in general, be grazed most and over a longer period of time during the grazing season or the year. The range manager will be greatly aided by close observance of such areas as a basis for his management judgment.

Chapter 4

RANGE FORAGE QUALITY AFFECTS RANGE MANAGEMENT

Satisfying nutritional requirements of range livestock in range forage. Fortifying range forage with essential constituents for animal nutritional requirements. The influence that quality of range forage has on both range management and livestock production. Characteristics of some range plants that make them significant to range management. Range forage consumption, the key to productive management. Amounts of forage a range animal will consume in a day.

A productive range is one that furnishes an adequate amount of forage of a quality that will meet the needs of grazing animals. An overabundance of poor quality forage will not necessarily provide animal body requirements, nor will an inadequate amount of good quality forage provide those requirements. There must be a reasonable balance between quantity and quality of forage for efficiency of livestock production, if the ranching operation is to be profitable. In the interest of good range management, such a balance is a variable factor that must be taken into account.

NUTRITIONAL NEEDS OF LIVESTOCK IN RANGE FORAGE

Animal nutrition can be considered from the standpoint of three requirements: maintenance, growth and fattening, and reproduction. Meeting these requirements is essential, whether the management enterprise be grazing, feedlot, or any combination of the two.

Also necessary are protein for the building and maintenance of body tissues; fats and carbohydrates for the production of heat and energy; minerals for the building and maintenance of bone, and to insure a multiplicity of body functions; and vitamins, which are essential to normal body functions.

Of the many minerals essential in livestock feeds, calcium and phosphorous are of greatest importance. A deficiency will impair bone development and body functions, and can cause numerous diseases. This was, no doubt, a reason for early research to determine the importance of calcium and phosphorous, and of suitable feed supplements, in insuring adequate supplies in livestock rations. These elements, along with other supplements, are now commonly provided in livestock feed, both in the feedlot and on the range.

Ordinarily, the essential mineral elements of the animal diet are in adequate supply in the components of common feedstuff, including good range forage. However, deficiencies of one or more of these elements may occur, to the detriment of the animal. Physical deterioration can usually be traced to the specific element or elements that are deficient, and they can be added to the feed in a suitable supplemental form.

Sometimes a deficiency in certain mineral elements in range soils is strongly reflected in the grazing quality of the forage produced. A deficiency of calcium and phosphorous is reflected in poor livestock production. Often a deficiency is great enough not only to lower the quality of the forage but to lower the palatability to the point that very little, if any, grazing use is made of that forage (Fig. 23). In either instance, these factors have a very direct bearing on the management of those ranges for efficient livestock production.

The vitamin complex common to most properly selected livestock feeds is essential to satisfactory livestock production. Of greatest importance are vitamin A and vitamin D, deficiencies of which can have a deleterious effect on livestock production.[1] The primary sources of vitamin A are corn and sorghum grain, with other than white endosperm, and the green color or chlorophyll in forage grasses and well preserved hay.[2] Vitamin D comes primarily from sunlight, although it can be synthesized from organic substances.

Owing to the source of both vitamins A and D, the presence or absence of them in the animal diet become factors in range management. This is particularly true of vitamin A. In much of the range

[1] Texas Agricultural Experiment Station *Bulletin* No. 630 (1943).

[2] *Vitamin A Studies with Beef Cattle* (Oklahoma State University Bulletin B-578, June, 1961).

Fig. 23. A luxuriant production of little bluestem that will not be grazed because of very low mineral content of the soil on which it is growing. (Photo courtesy USDA Soil Conservation Service, Texas.)

country where droughts are common, frequent seasonal fluctuation in growth and nongrowth of range forage can result in vitamin deficiencies. Likewise, forage produced under a canopy of forest trees or brush infested ranges very often is lacking in both vitamin A and D. And, animals grazing mostly in the shade may not be adequately fortified with vitamin D through normal body functions. These conditions are significant to management and use of those ranges. They may also be indicative of range treatment needs.

QUALITY OF RANGE FORAGE IN PRODUCTION MANAGEMENT

From the standpoint of livestock feed requirements, the quality of the range forage available is highly important to management of both the range and the livestock. Ranges are usually evaluated for grazing purposes in terms of acres per animal for a given period of time, usually a year. However, where planned grazing systems are used, pounds of forage per day, per month, or per year is given consideration. Regardless of the unit of measure, nutritional requirements available to the animal determine profit or loss from the enterprise.

Soil deficiencies of elements essential to both plant production and the diet of animals that graze those plants should be of great concern to the range manager. Not only do such deficiencies adversely affect the total food value of the forage, but seasonal palatability, total

TABLE 1
Chemical Analysis of Range Grasses—SCS Region 4, Fort Worth, Texas, 1950.*

SPECIES	CRUDE PROTEIN YOUNG	MATURE	DORM.	PHOSPHORUS YOUNG	MATURE	DORM.	CALCIUM YOUNG	MATURE	DORM.	POTASH YOUNG	MATURE	DORM.
Western wheatgrass		18.06			.16			.29				
Cane bluestem	3.44	3.31	3.00	.06	.13	.03	.27	.36	.22	.45	.37	
Sand bluestem		2.88			.09			.52			.66	
King ranch bluestem	10.93	5.51	6.13	.17	.15	.07	.78	.21	.56	.69		
Little bluestem	7.33	3.75	2.90	.11	.07	.05	.56	.52	.59	1.09	.49	.18
Red threeawn		1.48			.02			.20				
Sideoats grama	10.76	6.02	5.45	.16	.08	.06	.59	.58	.51		.16	
Black grama	8.31	5.86	5.56	.15	.09	.07	.58	.47	.38	.99	.68	
Blue grama	9.68	6.98	5.18	.23	.12	.07	.51	.51	.42			
Buffalograss	10.94	7.67	6.66	.13	.11	.07	.56	.67	.54		.21	
Bermudagrass	14.15	10.25	6.52	.27	.20	.17	.48	.50	.31	2.22		.34
Weeping lovegrass	7.38	5.14	3.33	.10	.07	.05	.39	.42	.45		.30	
Tanglehead	8.42	8.85	4.15	.09	.07	.04	.39	.32	.34	1.17		
Tobosagrass	7.94	8.94	4.09	.18	.13	.08	.66	.58	.45	.59	.60	.46
Bush muhly	10.11	3.50	6.67	.11	.09	.05	.47	.29	.33	1.06	.74	
Vine mesquite	7.83	5.96		.19	.13		.54	.46				
Switchgrass	10.96	5.62		.26	.07		.34	.25		1.88		
Indiangrass	11.89	6.26	3.19	.25	.14	.06	.39	.20	.69	1.99	1.43	.32
Johnsongrass	17.28	8.00		.37	.15		.82	.83		1.86		
Alkali sacaton	10.76	7.81	4.58	.06	.07	.05	.79	.65	.62	1.13	.66	
Mesa dropseed	10.75	6.06	5.93	.18	.09	.07	.60	.38	.32			.65
Texas wintergrass	9.38	10.66	6.63	.10	.11	.09	1.02	.69	.65			
New Mexico feathergrass	7.75	5.70	5.82	.05	.04	.04	.54	.43	.39			

*Courtesy—U.S. Soil Conservation Service, Texas.

forage required to meet animal needs, and growth and production from the livestock become limiting factors of management.

In recognition of the basic food requirements for livestock production, some knowledge of the chemical makeup of range forage is necessary. It is important to know which of the essential elements are in various forage plants as well as the amount and the degree of fluctuation from one stage of growth to another. Seasonal nutritive and palatability qualities of range forage is one of the most important principles of range management.

Results of plant analyses made by M. F. Wichman, soil scientist, and R. E. Fox, plant physiologist, with the Soil Conservation Service, Western Gulf Region, Fort Worth, Texas, are indicative of the seasonal fluctuation that takes place in forage plants. Table 1 gives this information for some twenty-three range grasses common to the area studied, which included the states of Texas, Oklahoma, Arkansas, and Louisiana.

Although the data recorded in Table 1 were collected over four states and over a period of approximately three years, the record is not complete. This is due to the fact that it was not always possible to collect adequate samples representing the three seasons of development in the same proximity where previous samples had been taken. However, the data do point up variations in nutritive content among species within a given developmental stage of the plant. Whether these differences are inherent to the species, are due to climatic differences, or are due to soil differences is not important as far as the results are concerned. What is important is the fact that differences do occur that are important to management of the range and the livestock.

THE INFLUENCE OF PLANT SPECIES ON FORAGE MANAGEMENT

The kind of plants very largely dictates the kind of management necessary to get the most out of the range without damaging results. Ranges in a low condition are more intricate in their management requirements than ranges in a higher condition. This is obvious because of the usually wide variety of low-quality plants that have invaded the low-condition range. It is a matter of getting the most out of those plants when they are palatable and nutritious, as indicated by livestock grazing preference.

In contrast to slipshod management of a range ("take all you can get when you can get it"), precise management requires that attention be given each group of range plants. This is the key to proper management of a range, regardless of its condition at the time.

On any range there are the "best" plants. On a poor condition range, all plants may be of poor quality, but there are those that are a little better than any of the rest, as indicated by grazing preference. This preference may vary among the plants that are there from one season to another. A knowledge of these seasonal preference changes, or preferences common to different kinds of livestock, is necessary to achieve the best management of that range.

At least a working knowledge of the forage plants on a range enables the range manager to exercise good judgment in his management decisions. Such knowledge should include an understanding of: the times when various plants are palatable and nutritious; the times when they will not be grazed by choice; the quality of forage they provide; the relative amount of feed available; and the growth requirements of those plants. Anything short of this basic knowledge of plant development, and response to its environment and treatment, is equivalent to leaving the management of the range to the livestock that uses it.

Regardless of whether the management of the range is planned according to its known needs or the range is just grazed, there will continue to be those "best" plants. They very likely will be selected first, will be used most, and generally will be grazed over a longer period of time. If free grazing is permitted, no consideration will be given their essential growth requirements. Yet, these are the key plants about which something can be done in the grazing and management of that range.

On the other hand, in a planned management system, it is these same "best" plants that are the key to the desired use of the range. They are recognized in the composition; their growth requirements are known; and their response to grazing and other environmental conditions are known. The grazing use that will be made of these plants, by choice, must be known at least to a practical degree. That is, it is essential to know approximately when they will be a first-choice plant for grazing; how closely they will be grazed and the probable frequency of repeat grazing; when, within the growing season, grazing of these plants would be discontinued; what regrowth might be expected; what the grazing extent is of other plants that occur in the composition; and, perhaps of major importance, how much grazing these key plants, along with other plants that would be used, will provide. That is, what would be the grazing capacity of that range for that grazing season, without over-use and range de-

CHARACTERISTICS OF SOME RANGE PLANTS
SIGNIFICANT TO MANAGEMENT

To point up the significance of various plants to range use and management, a number of examples are cited along with their characteristics that make them important.

Blue grama. One of the most widely distributed grasses throughout the southwest and plains states, it is characterized by being adapted to a rather severe climatic environment. It is a producer of fine stems and abundant foliage, and is nutritious and palatable over a long grazing season. In areas of low rainfall, it may remain palatable and nutritious through a period of two or more years. Thus, from the management standpoint, it is available over a long grazing period if properly managed (Fig. 24).

Little bluestem. On a fertile soil with adequate moisture conditions, it produces an abundance of highly palatable and nutritious feed. After maturity and during dormancy, its grazing preference declines, often to the extent of non-use other than winter browsing of seed heads and small amounts of foliage, perhaps for filler (Fig. 25). This characteristic dictates spring and summer use of this grass for greatest efficiency from livestock production. Owing to the diverse soil and climatic conditions where little bluestem will thrive, it is important to know its nutritive quality at that location before planning management. It may be productive on a soil that is low in some plant food elements. To this extent, its value for grazing may be misleading.

Sand bluestem. It is among the most palatable and highly nutritious of the tall grasses. It forms comparatively few growth buds on the underground portion of stems; therefore, regrowth during a growing season is somewhat limited. It is a strong tillering grass that aids in maintaining a productive stand. Since stems become very coarse and woody with maturity, they are less palatable. Nutritional quality declines rather rapidly with maturity and dormancy. It is one of the

Fig. 24. A blue grama range in mid-winter of the second year after this grass crop was produced. A properly managed range of good quality grasses in a comparatively dry climate will remain palatable and nutritious for two or three years during a prolonged drought. (Photo courtesy U.S. Soil Conservation Service, Texas.)

best and most productive grasses of southwestern sandy soils. Grazing to a degree where the livestock are ahead of the grass from early stages of growth throughout the growing season is usually detrimental to the stand, but when properly grazed from beginning of spring growth to dormancy, a sustained production of high quality forage can be maintained.

Western wheatgrass. A cool season grass, with potentially high nutritive quality, it is especially valuable for fall and early spring grazing use. When it occurs in abundance within a grazing unit, that unit should be given strong consideration for use other than during the summer months, in a grazing management plan (Fig. 26). Its resistance to grazing is much less than that of other grasses, owing to

Fig. 25. Unused little bluestem at the end of the grazing season (April 1). Blue grama and sideoats grama have been grazed excessively during winter months.

Fig. 26. Western wheatgrass in very early spring makes excellent grazing during a usually critical period on most ranges.

Fig. 27. *Texas wintergrass nearing maturity in early summer. Note the excessive production of seed and rough, bristly awns that sometimes are objectionable to grazing at this season. (Photo courtesy U.S. Soil Conservation Service, Texas.)*

the very high elevation of the growth point of vegetative stems. They are readily grazed, thereby ending regrowth of that stem.

Texas wintergrass. This grass, also being a cool season species, has the same general characteristics as western wheatgrass. Where adapted, it has the ability to maintain a comparatively high protein content up to full maturity, along with comparatively high forage production. Immediately following maturity, there is a profuse amount of very rough and bristly awns that impair grazing (Fig. 27), and are damaging to the fleece of sheep. This is a valuable range grass where it is adapted, but also one that requires precise and timely management if the most is to be gotten from it and from the livestock that use that range.

Threeawn species. There are numerous species of threeawn through-out the range country. They vary quite widely as to grazing value, but are generally considered among the less desirable range grasses. However, they do have a characteristic that gives added value to a range, especially where winter moisture is normally available: earli-ness of the start of spring growth in comparison to other warm season grasses. This single characteristic of a low-quality grass, when prop-erly managed and used, changes it into a range asset for the grazing unit. The nutritive quality of the range is greatly enhanced at a usually critical period.

Weeping lovegrass. This is an introduced grass that is used in some areas for seeding purposes. It is a prolific producer of both seed and forage, but its palatability and nutritive quality may be low, especial-

Fig. 28. Weeping lovegrass is one of the better grasses for returning depleted land to a protective cover. Its grazing value will vary with the quality of the land. (Photo courtesy Texas Tech University.)

ly on some depleted soils where it has proved to be one of the better grasses for seeding (Fig. 28). Experience has shown that under these conditions of growth and production, this warm season grass can best be used during the winter months. Here again, this is attributed largely to the protection afforded early development of green shoots as a result of non-use during the previous growing season. This non-use may be because of deferment of the pasture or it may be due to a lack of palatability during the latter part of the growing season, which is often the case.

Black grama. It is one of the better grasses of the southwest and is often associated with blue grama. The two may be in a well-balanced mixture, or black grama may be in a pure stand on certain sites. A significant value of this grass is the fact that it is a warm season grass,

Fig. 29. A black grama range in southwestern New Mexico that was deferred for use during the winter months. (Photo courtesy U.S. Soil Conservation Service, New Mexico.)

but carries over much of its green chlorophyll and carotene content through the winter months. This substance is retained in the base of each stem, extending up the stem three to six inches. Thus, it is a choice grass to be reserved for winter use where it is adapted (Fig. 29).

In all range areas, there are individual plants and groups of plants with distinct characteristics that make them significant for grazing use and management. They may be grasses, forbs, or browse plants, all of which are important to the range. Naturally, they will vary from one locality to another, as a result of environmental adaptation. There are, however, two groups of plants that become significant to management in any environmental adaptation: short-lived annual weeds, and poisonous plants. Annual weeds create a problem whenever they occur to any extent on rangeland. Their role in a management program is simply that of use to the extent livestock will graze them at the time they are palatable and will be taken by choice. A rule of thumb is that this time and amount generally occurs about the time lush spring growth starts in a locality. At that time, because livestock have been deprived of green feed during the winter, they are not too choosy as to what they graze. This prevails until their depleted body requirements have been met, or until weeds become unpalatable with maturity, and animals become more selective in their grazing pattern of the better forage plants. Sheep and goats may prolong this period of selective use of weeds, owing to their natural choice of weedy plants in conjunction with grass as their base diet. Where poisonous plants occur, grazing of those areas must be avoided during the period of toxicity. This period may be year-long, it may be season-long, or it may be rather brief, as is characteristic of shinnery oak poisoning during the bloom stage in parts of West Texas. These problems are generally local and must be dealt with on that basis.

RANGE FORAGE CONSUMPTION KEY TO
PRODUCTIVE MANAGEMENT

In evaluating range plants for grazing purposes, qualitative characteristics are more important than forage yields. Also, it is the quality of range forage that determines the amount necessary to meet the needs of livestock. Nutritional studies have determined the relative amounts of various food elements (proteins, carbohydrates, minerals, and vitamins) required for animal production.[3] These requirements have been identified by amounts required for maintenance, growth, and fattening, and for reproduction for various kinds of domestic livestock.

Additional nutritional requirement studies have been made to determine selectivity of grazing. Nelson, Herbel, and Jackson made such a study on the Jornada Experimental Range in southern New Mexico.[4] The pattern of grazing was that plants were selected when highest in essential elements to meet body needs, irrespective of whether the selected plant was grass, forb, or browse. The study also revealed that the wide variety of plants on the range made it possible for nutritional needs of the animal to be met throughout the year. Forbs and browse plants contributed much of the required mineral elements during the dormancy of grasses when they were deficient in these elements. Thus, a wide variety of plants to provide selective grazing materially added to the quality of the range.

Watkins, at New Mexico State University, made studies to determine the amount of representative range forage that would be required to supply body needs of livestock using the range. He arrived at a figure of 19.5 pounds of air dry forage to maintain an 887-pound cow.[5]

Youngblood and Cox determined that it would require approximately 20 pounds of air dry forage from the Edwards Plateau of Texas to maintain a 1000-pound cow.[6] These and perhaps other available basic data may be used to convert maintenance requirements to other kinds and classes of livestock with reasonable accuracy.

Production requirements over and above maintenance can be had only by an increase in the amounts of nutrients in the diet of the

[3] P. E. Neale, *Nutrition in Relation to the Utilization of Range Forage* (New Mexico State University Agricultural Experiment Station Bulletin 910, 1940).

[4] A. B. Nelson, C. H. Herbel, and H. M. Jackson, *Chemical Composition of Forage Species Grazed by Cattle on an Arid New Mexico Range* (New Mexico State University Agricultural Experiment Station Bulletin 561, 1970).

[5] W. E. Watkins, *The Calcium and Phosphorus Content of Important New Mexico Range Forages* (New Mexico State University Experiment Station Technical Bulletin 246, 1937).

[6] B. Youngblood and A. B. Cox, *An Economic Study of a Typical Ranching Area on the Edwards Plateau of Texas* (Texas Agricultural Experiment Station Bulletin 297, 1922) .

animal. Seasonal variations in the nutrient content of forage plants can generally be relied on to provide these increased needs, especially when livestock production coincides with seasonal fluctuations of plant growth. But this is not always possible. Much of the animal reproduction requirements occur during the season of normally low plant nutrient content. Neither can growth and fattening always be confined to the season of a high level of plant nutrients alone.

These facts impose the necessity of greater intake in pounds of range forage to provide the added food requirements for production in excess of maintenance. This added requirement can be met only by making available for grazing an amount of forage over and above maintenance needs. Such increased forage requirement is a point of management seldom taken into account in arriving at grazing rates. Also, the quality of these excess grazing needs may impose production limitations. That is, the kind of forage plants may be such as to require a volume greater than the intake capacity of the animal, to obtain the needed nutritive requirements. Some grasses have a very high lignin or fiber content that declines to a very low mineral content with dormancy. It is next to impossible for an animal to consume enough of this type of forage to meet even body maintenance requirements.

HOW MUCH FORAGE WILL AN ANIMAL CONSUME IN A DAY?

From the standpoint of production efficiency and stable ranching operations, the rancher must be concerned with proper management of both his range and his livestock. This means the highest possible sustained production of range forage with proper utilization of it for maximum livestock production without damage to the range. It is a recognized fact that approximately 50 per cent, by volume weight, of a plant must be left unused at the end of the grazing season for maintenance of the plant. This means only half of the total production can be safely utilized by grazing animals. Therefore, in determining grazing values or carrying capacities of ranges, pounds of forage produced and pounds of forage required must be considered for a reasonably accurate determination to be made.

The logical question is: How much forage will an animal eat in a day? The answer depends on the kind and size of the animal and the kind and quality of the forage, as discussed above. Although wide

TABLE 2
Air Dry Range Forage Consumption Per Day

KIND AND CLASS OF LIVESTOCK	ANIMAL UNIT EQUIVALENT	MAINTENANCE RATION (LBS/DAY)	PRODUCTION RATION (LBS/DAY)
Cattle			
Weaned calves and yearlings	.60	12.00	16.0–21.0
Mature cows with or without			
unweaned calf	1.00	20.00	27.0–32.0
Steers, 600 to 900 pounds	1.00	20.00	24.0–30.0
Bulls, 2 years and over	1.30	26.00	30.0–36.0
Horses			
Yearlings	.75	15.00	20.0–26.0
Two years old	1.00	20.00	27.0–35.0
Three years old and over	1.25	25.00	31.0–43.0
Sheep, Goats, & Deer			
Weaned lambs, kids, or			
yearlings	.12	2.40	2.5–3.3
Ewes or does with or without			
unweaned lambs or kids	.20	4.00	4.5–6.0
Rams or bucks	.26	5.20	6.0–7.0
Deer with or without			
unweaned fawns	.20	4.00	4.5–6.0

variations do occur, it is only practical to arrive at a requirement figure commensurate with the kind of livestock and kind of forage at hand.

On the basis of research information cited above, in both Texas and New Mexico, approximately 20 pounds of air dry forage per day is required maintenance of a 900- to 1,000-pound cow. Such a figure may well be considered a fair average for the quality of forage common to much of the range country, and particularly the southwest. This being for maintenance only, it is readily understood that something above that amount would be required if either growth and fattening or reproduction is to be achieved. Here again, the amount over and above a maintenance ration is a matter of conjecture, depending on the quality of the forage. However, experience and grazing capacity standards indicate that an increase up to 50 per cent in forage consumption is required for profitable livestock production. Thus, a 50 per cent increase over the established 20 pounds per day would be a 30-pound requirement of air dry feed, for a mature cow.

Stocking rates, grazing capacities, and range forage requirements are generally dealt with in terms of animal units. An animal unit has been established as a 900-pound range cow with a calf to weaning age. All other kinds and classes of domestic livestock and wild game that use range forage have been related to the animal unit on the basis of their feed requirements. Table 2 shows animal unit equivalents with a maintenance ration of 20 pounds per day per animal for a production ration. Grazing observations, range forage yields, range utilization surveys, and grazing capacity experience substantiate these projected requirements.

When the various factors of production and harvest are taken into account, total range forage production must be sufficient to perform all the requirements of the range resource.

It is only through experience and evaluation that a reliable forage production and stocking rate can be arrived at for a particular range. As a general guide, based on experience over much of the southwestern range country, an average figure of 30 to 32 pounds of air dry range forage per day per animal unit is a fairly conservative figure. This allows for a margin of wastage that is inevitable, even with good management.

Using an average figure of 31 pounds, the use requirement for a month is approximately 1,000 lbs. If good management is to be practiced, approximately 50 per cent by volume weight of forage will be left for maintenance of the plant and protection to the land. Thus, the total production needed is approximately 2,000 pounds, or one ton per month for each mother cow, with or without her calf to weaning age. Requirements for other kinds and classes of livestock can be arrived at by applying their animal unit equivalent to the above rule of thumb requirement.

Chapter 5

RANGE SITE AND CONDITION
EVALUATION OF RANGELAND

Recognition of the need for preservation of rangelands in the United States. Early stages in the development of range inventories and surveys. The range site and range condition concept, and its development as a procedure for evaluating rangelands. Characteristics of a range site and the ways range sites differ. Range condition and plant response to grazing. Determining the ecology of a range site and a logical grouping of plants to evaluate range condition. Identifying range sites and range conditions as a basis for range management.

From the very beginning of the use of native grasslands for grazing by domestic livestock, those lands were evaluated by the "eyeball" method, with no specific unit of measure. Yet, they were given values on a comparative basis of one area with another. They were recognized as deteriorating or improving over a period of time. They were and still are, in too many instances, evaluated as to condition by response to rainfall or lack of rainfall.

Based on economic returns from the land, these evaluations, in general, proved to be reasonably accurate in the early days of the ranching industry. However, such evaluations have been financially disastrous to many ranchers, because not until the damage was done could the final evaluation be made.

This is to say that to the early day rancher, grass was grass, and if it rained, the condition of the range was good, but if rainfall was insufficient, conditions were bad. Along with this judgment, evaluation was recognition that one part of the country produced grass in greater abundance than some other area. It was also recognized that different areas produced different kinds of grasses, some tall, some short, some with coarse stems, and some with fine stems. Some grasses were more palatable than others. Some were more nutritious and stock gained better on them than on others. And of particular significance to the rancher was the fact that some grass grew on one kind of land but not on another kind.

Through the years, these values, and perhaps many others, were recognized by users and managers of native grasslands. Ranchers were often proficient in making these evaluations, as evidenced by many successful years in the ranching business.

Much of this success can be attributed to close observation, good judgment, and experience, rather than to any specific criteria of or evaluation of what was actually taking place on those grasslands. Furthermore, this rancher knowledge and experience has been invaluable to those who have, in more recent years, developed procedures whereby rangelands can be precisely evaluated.

THE BEGINNING OF RANGELAND PRESERVATION

Very early in the domestic use of grazing lands in the western United States, deterioration and threatened destruction of public range and allied resources was noted. Consequently, in 1891 Congress authorized the President to set aside areas of "forest reserves." These areas have since been designated as national forests. By this act the federal government assumed the responsibility of preserving and improving the timber, the forage, and other resources of the forests.

This was the beginning of more careful and precise observations and recordings of the components of the range. Rather than a range just having grass, in abundance or in sparse stands, it had specifically different kinds or species of grass. Rather than having only grass, there might also be shrubs, forbs, and even trees that provide grazable forage. Even at that early date, those responsible for the preservation of these lands recognized changes, sometimes drastic and rapid, taking place among various kinds of plants on the range. Thus, there was a challenge to determine the results of grazing on rangeland and a way of recording changes that might have taken place. Such information would serve for more accurate evaluations and projected use of those lands.

From this beginning there was a continuing recognition of the need for the preservation and the improvement of much of the grazing land of the west. Additional lands were designated as forest reserves, including many acres that were not forest but grazing resources. By 1921 the total area had expanded to over 156,500,000 acres within the boundaries of national forests.

Since that date, other lands have been included in national forests, and, in addition, vast areas of land for other uses have been brought under the supervision of both state and national jurisdiction. Areas of administration include provisions of the Taylor Grazing Act. Bureau of Land Management, lease arrangements of individual states, and, although not specifically for grazing purposes, protective areas such as national parks and recreation areas.

Early administration of these lands was not always to the benefit of the grazing resource. This was not because of a lack of concern and policy, but primarily to a lack of understanding and knowledge of the response of grazing lands to grazing use and related environments of an area.

Much has been achieved, and guidelines have been published, on establishing techniques and procedures for evaluating rangeland. Such information was to serve as a basis for management commensurate with rapidly developing needs for preservation. Perhaps the first concrete and established procedure for rangeland evaluation was the grazing reconnaissance developed by the U.S. Forest Service in the early years of that agency. The purpose of the grazing reconnaissance was to determine and record what the grazing resources were, where they were, what their true grazing value was, and how they could best be utilized and improved. From the reconnaissance, information was obtained as to physical features, climatic conditions, need for watershed protection, character, abundance of forest and forage resources, and a classification of the land into vegetation types. The first organized party to make such a reconnaissance was formed in 1911, when a study was initiated on the Coconino National Forest in northern Arizona under the leadership of James T. Jardine.

From these grazing reconnaissance procedures, range inventory techniques were improved, becoming much more precise and more informative as to the grazing value of the resource. With this development there emerged what came to be known as the Western Range Survey.

Western Range Survey procedures became the standard used by all agencies that had responsibilities for inventorying grazing lands. Techniques used served very well, in that ranges were rather uniformly categorized as to the resources at hand and current grazing values. Perhaps the most significant fallacy of the evaluation was the fact that livestock did not graze the range exactly according to either the abundance or the palatability of the various forage plants as recorded in the inventory. Although factors were derived representing forage acres available and forage acre requirements by kinds of livestock, it was not possible to accurately interpret their values throughout the grazing year.

These shortcomings of inventory procedures were readily recognized, not only by those using them but by those who developed them. This brought about a very intense effort, particularly by research people and technical field scientists, to improve or develop new range inventory procedures.

THE RANGE SITE AND RANGE CONDITION CONCEPT AND ITS DEVELOPMENT

Numerous ideas were developed as a method of range inventory that could be interpreted into practical guidance to grazing use. Very early the concept of the range site and range condition inventory showed promise. However, in the early stages of development as a procedure, techniques were questionable.

Fallacies existed because numerous separations of the range were made based on several factors that were decidedly variable. Also, at that time it was difficult to escape from the "range type" concept which was primarily a vegetative aspect. The range type inventory identified plants that were found and indicated their relative abundance. But they were not related specifically to a kind of soil and available water. Consequently, the inventory might lump into a single unit of evaluation two or more distinctly different kinds of rangeland as to the potential vegetation and grazing values.

The multiple factor procedure for judging range condition was somewhat confusing. Too many degrees of condition requiring fine lines of separation resulted in wide variance in judgment among technicians making range inventories. Such factors as species composition, density of stand, vigor of plants, accumulation of litter or mulch, soil condition, erosion, and compaction were considered in the evaluation. When the degrees of condition added to these, as indicated by ratings such as excellent, very good, high good, good, low good, high fair, fair, low fair, poor, and very poor, an inventory could become meaningless. It was difficult to reach any degree of uniformity in interpreting the range inventory, even among well-qualified range technicians.

The range site and range condition concept remained somewhat dormant in favor of the western range survey, as far as wide-scale range inventories were concerned, until about 1940. At that time flood control surveys became a responsibility of the Soil Conservation Service. Among the first surveys were those initiated on the Colorado River and North Concho River in central west Texas. Since both time and money were limiting factors in the completion of these surveys, it became evident that the time consuming and intricate details of western range survey procedures were not practical. It was determined that a more practical procedure would have to replace the established range inventory procedures if the collection of range information was to keep pace with other segments of the survey.

The range site and range condition concept offered the most logical procedure to meet this challenge. It was currently being given high priority by interested agencies and institutions in developmental procedures.

ECOLOGIC BASIS FOR RANGE SITE AND RANGE CONDITION CLASSES

By 1944 the use of the range site and condition class was being used quite extensively in Soil Conservation Service Region 4,* and to an increasing degree, in other SCS regions where rangelands were important. In the early stages of development, greater emphasis had been placed on accuracy in describing range condition classes than had been given in recognizing and describing range sites. Generally, kinds of land was used to identify a range site.

In 1944 Dr. E. J. Dyksterhuis, range specialist with the Soil Conservation Service at Fort Worth, Texas, was assigned to make a detailed evaluation of the ecology, present condition, and potential of the West Cross Timbers area of north central Texas, as grazing land.

With a background of work done by a number of noted plant scientists, an objective was established to determine an infallible basis on which range condition criteria could be established.

* Texas, Oklahoma, Louisiana, and Arkansas.

At this stage in the development of a procedure for evaluating rangelands, there came to light an admixture of factors indicative of the status of the range. They fell into two general categories: those having to do with the presence or absence of kinds and amounts of plants on the range, and those having to do with production. Factors in the first category may be briefly identified as: plant succession as established by Dr. F. E. Clements and others; kinds of rangeland as projected by Sampson; types of vegetation as identified by Aldus and Schantz for semi-arid areas; degrees of grazing as recognized by Renner from the Santa Fe National Forest Survey in New Mexico; Talbot's work on plant indicators for southwest range conditions; and Stoddard's five classes of range condition as related to the climax for range types in the Pacific northwest. Factors in the second category included range productivity, plant density, animal gains and calving percentages, vigor of plants, amount of soil protecting litter accumulated, and stability of the soil or the degree of soil erosion.

Thus, there was a conglomerate of factors being considered, particularly in evaluating range condition. Each of these factors, or groups of factors, had some merit and some individuals who completely supported each of them.

With due consideration of viewpoints and the various factors that evolved, what seemed to be an adequate criterion for range evaluations was identified. The factors included grazing capacity, plant density, plant vigor, soil erosion, soil tilth, animal gains and calving percentages, and composition of plant cover.

In Dyksterhuis's work in the West Cross Timbers of Texas, most of these factors began to prove unreliable as a unit of measure, for one reason or another. The primary inadequacy of most of them was the lack of uniformity and consistency from one area to another, or from one year or season to another.

The one factor that filtered out as being most reliable and practical was that having to do with the composition of plant cover. However, other factors being used were not without value, as they, when considered in light of plant composition, serve reliably to indicate the trend in range condition. Trend, or the direction, rate, and degree of the change in range condition is often just as important as the condition itself in projecting a range management program.

THE RANGE SITE

Of first importance in classifying a range is the recognition of differences of kinds of land or the range site. This means that each different kind of land, even within the same climate, has its own potential as to the kinds and amounts of plants that grew there originally. When there is a change in these kinds and amounts of plants with undisturbed conditions, there is another range site (Figs. 30 and 31). This alone provides an ecologic basis for classifying rangeland, or any other land use supporting native vegetation, such as forest lands or recreation lands.

Ecology provides a basis for dividing any land area, whether it be a continent, a region, a state, or merely localized range sites, into areas of distinct natural plant cover characteristics. These are recognized as the ecologic climax for the respective area; thus, there is the climax for each area of land which is known or can be determined. In addition to establishing the original plant composition or climax unit for a land area, ecology also identifies the different plant communities that successively occupy those land areas, that is, changes in plant composition that occur as an area moves from the climax down to bare ground, or from bare ground back toward the climax.

Fig. 30. A deep sand site where tall grasses as sand bluestem, Indiangrass, and switchgrass predominate when in top condition.

Fig. 31. Sandy land site, in close proximity to the deep sand site in Fig. 30, both in the eastern Texas panhandle. Here the dominant grasses are little bluestem and sideoats grama with the tall grasses in lesser amounts when in top condition; thus, there is a different site.

Fig. 32. A bottom land site on the Canadian River. The potential of this site is a high production of tall grasses. With deterioration they will give way to short grasses, forbs, more tree growth, and eventually dense undergrowth and brush.

Fig. 33. A deep upland site of the Davis Mountain country of southwest Texas. Blue grama is the climax grass of this site, but with abusive use it will retrogress to threeawn, false buffalograss, and bare ground.

Fig. 34. A limestone hill site in a 9- to 13-inch rainfall belt of southwest Texas. Desert type shrubs and grasses are climax on this site. Black grama, a small sideoats grama, and some blue grama are management objectives for the site. With range deterioration, slim and hairy tridens and red grama become the dominant grasses.

Fig. 35. A desert shrub site in a 8- to 10-inch rainfall belt. Although black grama, hairy grama, and a small sideoats grama were climax to the site, only remnants of these can be found on this range. Creosote-bush and tarbush have become post climax to the site.

Succession of plant compositions toward a climax community under favorable range management and retrogression of the plant composition under destructive grazing use are natural responses that occur, with each range site having its own distinct characteristics (Figs. 32, 33, 34, 35). At any particular point in these events of change in succession and retrogression, the true condition of the range is evaluated as related to the ecological balance of the climax. That is, the climax unit is the highest and, when reduced to a bare area, that represents the lowest state of condition for that area of land. Therefore, it is logical to recognize some measure of range condition at any point between these extremes.

To describe accurately and minutely the plant composition at any particular point in the stage of succession or retrogression, with any degree of consistency, would be impossible. However, it is possible to identify the composition of plants within a given segment of the succession or retrogression scale as it moves to or from the climax unit. On this basis it is logical to make an arbitrary decision between the highest and lowest stages of plant development. A practical division seemed to be four segments of twenty-five increments each. To illustrate, the chart in Fig. 36 was developed by Dyksterhuis:

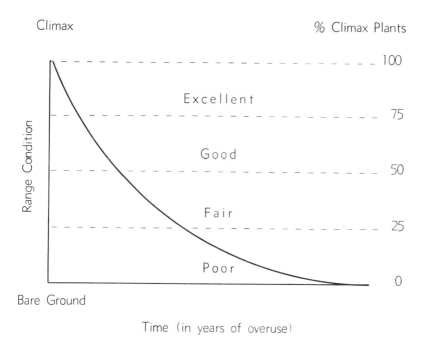

Fig. 36. A graphic evaluation of plant composition and range condition.

Inasmuch as this division embodies all factors which influence range condition, it is easy to identify four distinct range condition classes. For simplicity, and to be easily understood as to comparative values, they were identified as excellent, good, fair, and poor. However, naming them was not sufficient as a measure of range condition; something tangible was necessary for concrete evaluations.

The work of Dr. J. E. Weaver on the sensitivity of response to grazing by range plants seemed to be a most logical way of recognizing plant succession and thus stages of range condition.

Weaver found that plants respond differently when grazed by livestock, particularly if the grazing pressure is rather heavy. That is, if the degree of grazing of a species is in excess of the individual plant requirements for maintenance and regrowth of that plant, the plant response will have an effect on the entire range. In regard to response, range forage plants fall into three categories: (1) those that decrease in abundance with grazing pressure; (2) those that first increase in abundance then, with continued grazing pressure, decrease; (3) those that invade the range as plants of the first two categories are removed by grazing pressure. These invading plants may increase or decrease with continuous heavy grazing, but ultimately will decrease, even to the point of extinction of all edible plants. By this response to grazing by a plant composition, any range examined will fall somewhere along the curve of the above chart.

RANGE CONDITION AND PLANT RESPONSE TO GRAZING

In order to classify properly the plants that grow on a given area, it is necessary to know those plants and their individual response to grazing when growing in combination with one another, and as influenced by the prevailing climate. Grazing by domestic livestock introduces the factor of selectivity of plants. Animals will select and graze first those plants that are most palatable and nutritious. Such plants will receive 75 to 80 per cent of the grazing when it is possible for the animal to select what he prefers. Generally, these plants are the best that will grow on that site, thus they constitute the primary components of the climax unit. For the most part, they will be the taller growing, most accessible forage plants, and they will receive repeat grazing most often. These characteristics alone dictate the effect that heavy grazing of a climax range will have at the outset.

In addition to the most desirable plants, the climax unit of any range will have a percentage of plants of the second category. These are the plants that increase at the outset of grazing pressure. Usually they are second choice by grazing animals and are not too heavily grazed during the period the more desirable plants are being grazed to a point of decline in the composition. These secondary increaser plants move into the space left bare by decreaser plants that become less abundant in the stand. This represents the very first step in range deterioration from the climax unit.

Subsequently, with continued grazing pressure, the best climax decreaser plants will be selected to the extent of their production, along with the better increaser plants. Ultimately, continued pressure will cause the increaser plants to also decline in abundance because the degree of grazing them is over and above that required for maintenance of the individual plant. If this process continues, both decreaser and increaser plants will gradually be eliminated from the composition, leaving room for invading plants to take their place. They too will be subject to the same fate, especially those that may be fairly palatable and nutritious. And they too will be replaced by less palatable and possibly ungrazable or poisonous plants. In the absence of a source for undesirable plants, the range may revert to a barren waste.

A good example of a plant composition that represents the three grazing response categories of plants is the blue grama-buffalograss-threeawn combination common to much of the southern plains. As listed, these plants are in their response order of decreasers, increasers, and invaders, on many of the better sites.

It is the process of plant adjustments that results in the various categories of range condition as may occur on any range site. As discussed above, it will be the relative percentages of plants in the three categories of decreasers, increasers, and invaders that will evaluate a range site into its condition of excellent, good, fair, or poor.

ECOLOGY OF EACH RANGE SITE IMPORTANT TO RANGE EVALUATION

In order to classify and evaluate rangeland, it is necessary to recognize individual range sites and their identifying characteristics. Furthermore, it is necessary to know the important plants of that site and the response category to which each belongs.

Range sites are a kind of land within a given climatic zone. The kind of land is a combination of factors that result in the production of a plant composition composed of the kinds and amounts of plants that land, with its prevailing climate, will produce. These important land factors include depth of soil, texture and structure of soil, water and fertility holding capacity, inherent chemical and physical properties, and slope and exposure. Other soil factors, such as erosion and depleted fertility, along with low-quality plants, are indicators of range condition trends and may limit progressive improvement, but are not truly site factors.

It is important to know that range sites, in addition to land characteristics, are determined by the prevailing climate. That is, a given kind of land in a 25-inch rainfall belt may also occur in a 15-inch rainfall belt. However, they would be entirely different range sites because the kind and amount of forage plants would be different in the two areas, owing to rainfall. The difference may be reflected as to the kinds of plants produced, or in the amount of total production, either of which would dictate a different range site.

Knowing and describing range sites and range condition criteria requires a basic knowledge of the ecology of an area, along with training and experience in interpreting the landscape. Of primary importance in making accurate interpretations is a knowledge of range indicators. Although such indicators as reduced carrying capacity of the range, lowered calving percentages and beef production, severe soil and water losses, invasion of brush, increased feed bills are significant, they are correctly placed in the "too late" category. Once a range reaches a stage indicated by these factors, a reclamation job for that ranch is usually in order.

On the other hand, there are many useful indicators of the trend, and, in fact, the condition of the range that can be detected in the very early stages of development. This becomes a significant part of a range inventory and evaluation. Of equal importance is the value of these indicators to the rancher once he becomes familiar with them and their proper interpretation.

EVALUATING RANGE CONDITION

As described and illustrated by Fig. 36, four condition classes are recognized. The maximum plant composition which is the climax unit for a range site is given a value of 100 per cent. This means that such a plant composition is as good as that site can support and is logically considered excellent range condition. This condition would be made up primarily of those better forage plants of the decreaser category. Small percentages of the better increaser plants suited to that site would be present, but there would be no invaders. Thus, there is a maximum range condition and grazing resource, based on the vegetative composition alone. This too represents maximum ecological development and balance of nature that is possible for that range site, which is a result of the complexities of soil and climate resources.

From experience in range evaluations it has been found that when the percentage of decreaser plants is from 75 to 100, the amounts of increaser plants will not be sufficiently high to degrade the range either as to forage production or stability of the soil resource. Therefore, whenever the vegetation for any given range site consists of 75 per cent or more of the better decreaser plants, that range condition is considered to be excellent. Likewise, it has been possible to determine with a reasonable degree of accuracy the amounts of increaser plants that could be acceptable to have a range in excellent condition. These amounts then become the allowable percentage of the composition that increaser plants will be tolerated in determining range condition. Only that percentage of the total plant composition will be allowed in arriving at range condition values. The percentage of increaser plants above these allowables will be considered as invading plants, which will count against the range condition evaluation.

By this same line of reasoning, when climax decreaser plants plus allowable increaser plants make up from 50 to 75 per cent of the total plant composition, the condition of the range is considered good. When the percentage of those two plant response categories is from 25 to 50 per cent, the condition is fair. And when it is less than 25 per cent the condition is poor (Figs. 37, 38, 39, 40).

Here, then, is an ecological basis for determining range condition, one that does not vary within a range site. That is, the ecological development for a site does not vary as to its potential for the production of range forage. It is important, however, to understand that even though the potential does not vary appreciably, the plant composition for a site does vary from the potential, but these variations make different range conditions.

HOW THE ECOLOGY OF A RANGE SITE IS DETERMINED

To evaluate range conditions it becomes necessary to know the full ecological development of each different kind of land or range site. That is, it is essential to know the potential or climax unit for each range site as expressed as a kind of land within a given climate.

Excellent range condition is represented by truly climax vegetation as would be described by the ecologist. Furthermore, it represents the vegetation of a site after fully developed and mature, as would be measured over a long period of years and before disturbance of any kind. Seldom can there be found an area of land within the bounds of human population that has not been disturbed to one degree or another, by one means or another. Therefore, arriving at

Fig. 37. *Gravelly site, Knox County, Texas, in excellent range condition. Little bluestem, sand bluestem, sideoats grama, heath aster, dotted gayfeather, and prairie clover are decreaser and strong increaser plants that determine the range condition. (Photo courtesy U.S. Soil Conservation Service, Texas.)*

Fig. 38. *Gravelly site, Knox County, Texas, in good range condition. An increase in excess of the allowable amount of both little bluestem and sideoats grama, along with some invading plants, lowers the condition from excellent to good. (Photo courtesy U.S. Soil Conservation Service, Texas.)*

Fig. 39. *Gravelly site, Knox County, Texas, in fair range condition. Increaser plants are dominant on this site. The excess above the allowable amount of sideoats grama and buffalograss with numerous invaders lowers this range to fair condition. (Photo courtesy U.S. Soil Conservation Service, Texas.)*

Fig. 40. *Gravelly site, Knox County, Texas, in poor range condition. Here all decreasers and the better increaser plants have been grazed out, leaving only a sparse stand of secondary increasers and invaders. (Photo courtesy U.S. Soil Conservation Service, Texas.)*

true climax conditions for the many different range sites, even within a rather limited area, has been and continues to be a problem requiring the highest degree of ecological skill. Historical records, research in plant science, and keen observations and interpretations have been the basic tools by which this job is being done.

Within each climatic zone throughout the country it has been necessary for plant scientists to make these determinations to the best of their ability with information at hand. Such information is usually to be had if diligently sought after. A symbol of technical skill among these people is the location of a relict area that reflects its potential vegetation. A relict area is an undisturbed plot of land on which is found the vegetation of the climax unit. Such an area may never have been disturbed, or there may have been some disturbance, but near complete recovery has taken place. Fenced out areas inaccessible to grazing by any kind of livestock, old and often unkept cemeteries, preserves, and the like, usually provide the best concrete evidence of the climax unit for an area or range site. A relict area permits interpretations with a rather high degree of accuracy by the plant scientists trained in the field of ecology.

Through the years, the development of range condition descriptions has been among the greater challenges in the field of range conservation and management. It has also been a most excellent training device for range technicians. These descriptions also furnish valuable and understandable information to ranchers who have had the interest and taken the time to become conversant with the information obtained.

Although much has been achieved by way of accurately arriving at and describing the many hundreds of range sites and range conditions throughout the country, there is still much to be done. As range site and condition classes are used in the evaluation of range lands, improvements continue to be made. Refinements are being made in describing climax units of range sites, and in accuracy in interpreting plant responses to grazing, drought, or other disturbances. Experience in this field is being reflected in improved techniques and procedures for evaluating ranges and subsequent range improvement recommendations that are appropriate.

RANGE CONDITION CLASSES AND RANGE FORAGE YIELDS

These principles and procedures as discussed are basic to determining range condition, but are not intended as a means of determining or predicting range yields. Nevertheless, this system of classification is significant as to range production, in that plant communities highest in ecological succession are also capable of highest sustained production. Because of this, it generally follows that range condition will be indicative of range yields. However, there may be conditions where climax plants that are extremely sensitive to grazing will not remain in the composition sufficiently long to retain high production. Under such circumstances, plants of the increaser category may actually have a higher sustained forage production. In such instances the management objective possibly should be to achieve no higher than a good range condition.

In some southerly climates with moderately high rainfall, there frequently is a misconcept of range condition as influenced by range yields of both forage and livestock products. There may have been serious deterioration of the plant composition through heavy grazing or possibly a combination of disturbances. Because of mild climate and abundance of moisture, there may be a type of both increaser and invading plants that are palatable and nutritious that will occupy the space left bare by declining climax plants of the decreaser category. These may include, in addition to desirable increasers, both cool season and warm season annuals, in which case the range is essentially converted to an annual pasture. Although this condition is looked upon with favor by some operators, it should not be regarded as a satisfactory range condition. Even though production may be satisfactory for the type of operation at hand, it cannot be considered as a stable and ecologically sound capability of the range. Such situations should not be confused with the ecologic concept of classifying range condition. Here again, it is important to recognize the fact that continued heavy grazing use will eventually remove more palatable annual plants. They, in turn, will be replaced by less desirable plants from the grazing standpoint.

PLANT GROUPING AND EVALUATION IN DETERMINING RANGE CONDITION

To classify the condition of a range site, as pointed out above, it is necessary to know the plants that are to be found on that site, and especially those plants of the original or climax composition. This information could be obtained from a relict area, from published findings of plant ecologists, or from reliable interpretations of the vegetation that is there now, along with accurate retrogressive changes that have taken place. A first step would be to list the climax decreasers with the relative per cent each is to the total composition. A second listing would be those plants in the climax of the increaser category and the relative per cent each of these occupy in the original composition. In that these plants are generally of lesser stature than their coexisting climax decreasers when growing together in the climax, they do not, of their own accord, crowd out decreaser plants. Therefore, the percentage these plants would occupy in the climax would be comparatively small and rather stable. Generally 5 to 10 per cent, and never more than 25 per cent, of the climax would be increaser plants. Any percentage these plants make up over and above that found in the climax would be considered as invaders to the site. These excess percentages would be included with the invader category of plants.

A third listing would be plants that will invade or have invaded the site but are never found in the climax composition. In that they do not occur in the climax for the site, none are allowed for an excellent condition. Furthermore, any amounts of invading plants encountered in a classification take away from percentage of climax decreasers and increasers, thereby lowering the condition class. A simple listing of plants that would apply to the deep hardlands of the southern plains might be as follows:

DECREASERS	INCREASERS		INVADERS
Blue grama	Buffalograss	15%*	Threeawn
Sideoats grama	Silver bluestem	5%*	Sand dropseed
Vine mesquite	Galleta	5%*	Sand muhly
Western wheatgrass			Western ragweed
Climax forbs			Broom snakeweed

* Allowable percentage in the climax.

A pasture has been examined with the following composition. Decreasers: blue grama, sideoats grama, and vine mesquite, 35 per cent. Increasers: buffalograss, 25 per cent; silver bluestem, 10 per cent. Invaders: threeawn, 5 per cent; sand dropseed, 10 per cent; sand muhly, 5 per cent; broom snakeweed, 10 per cent. When analyzed, the condition class is found to be as follows:

	PERCENTAGE	TOTAL ALLOWED
Decreasers	35	35
Increasers	35	20
Invaders	30	0
	100	55

Therefore, with only 55 per cent of the total composition being climax for the site, the range condition is *good* (between 50 and 75 per cent by the classification chart, Fig. 36).

For purposes of clarification of the above calculation, it should be pointed out that only 20 per cent of the increasers were allowed in the climax from the plant classification chart (buffalograss, 15 per cent; silver bluestem, 5 per cent).

By this procedure each and every different range site would be evaluated for a grazing unit. This, in turn, gives a very satisfactory basis for arriving at appropriate range management. Rather reliable stocking rates, seasons of use, needed rest periods, and the class of livestock best suited are deductions that can be logically made from an analysis of various range sites and condition within a grazing unit.

The development and use of the range site and range condition concept in range management has been based on scientific investigations and the practical application of these findings. The following references, and many others, have been of great value in formulating standards and procedures:

1. Allred, B. W. *How To Classify Grasslands*. Range Fieldbook, Series III. USDA Soil Conservation Service, Fort Worth, Texas, 1947.

2. Allred, B. W. *Progress in Perfecting Range Condition Classes*. USDA Soil Conservation Service, Fort Worth, Texas, 1947.

3. Bell, Hershel M. and V. M. Douglas. *Wartime Ranching In Texas And Oklahoma*. USDA Soil Conservation Service, Fort Worth, Texas, 1942.

4. Bell, Hershel M. and E. J. Dyksterhuis. *Regional Range Handbook*. USDA Soil Conservation Service, Fort Worth, Texas, 1944.

5. Clements, Fredrick E. *Investigations In Ecology, 1928 And 1932*. Carnegie Institution Of Washington. Reprints from Yearbooks No. 27, pages 188–96 and No. 31, pages 211–17.

6. Dyksterhuis, E. J. *The Vegetation Of The Fort Worth Prairie*, January, 1946, and *The Vegetation Of The Western Cross Timbers*, July, 1948. USDA Soil Conservation Service, Fort Worth, Texas.

7. Renner, Fredrick G. *Survey Of Santa Fe National Forest*. U. S. Forest Service, 1922.

8. Renner, Fredrick G. and Eric A. Johnson. *Improving Range Conditions For Wartime Livestock Production*. USDA Soil Conservation Service, Farmers Bull. No. 1921, 1942.

9. Talbot, M. W. *Indicators Of Southwestern Range Conditions*. U. S. Forest Service, 1924.

10. Weaver, J. E. and Farrel A. Branson. *Quantitative Study Of Degeneration Of Mixed Prairie*. The Botanical Gazette, Vol. 14, June 1953.

Chapter 6

RANGE TRENDS AND INDICATORS

Change in the grazing aspect of ranges over the years. The relationship between range trends and range condition indicators. Significance of the ecological climax to the identity of range trends and range condition indicators. Grazing use influence on trends and condition of ranges. Management needs as dictated by indicators of both a declining and improving range condition. Normal plant reactions as range deterioration indicators.

Range is identified as land supporting native or adapted introduced forage plants that are harvested by grazing animals. Although at any given period of time it is a rather stable and static entity of the earth, it is in reality among the most dynamic of all natural resources. Each component of the range is a living thing. The soil becomes a living mass when teeming with many and varied organisms. When permeated by an abundance of plant roots, it responds to reactions and interactions of life giving organic and inorganic substances. It is the recipient and the giver of the life sustaining elements: air, light, and water. Without these elements, no living organisms within the soil, nor the vegetation that grows, nor animals that use that vegetation could have life. Thus, range is a living complex, yet it is as simple as any form of life, including plants, animals, and man himself.

Inasmuch as range is living and dynamic, it is constantly undergoing changes, changes that might be indiscernible even when closely observed. It is the accumulative process of these changes that eventually becomes recognizable and prominently evident as characteristics of the range. These changes, it is hoped, are for the betterment and improvement of the range. But all too often the reverse occurs, with range deterioration taking place.

Close observation, recognition, and interpretation of these telltale changes are important to sound range management, conservation, and highest production. Although many obscure changes take place, there is a cause. Therefore, it is important for the range manager to detect these changes in the very early stages of development. It is even more important that he know the influence that management of the range has on their occurrence. It is in this area that he has at least a reasonable degree of control. Range management becomes a procedure of using the range in such a way that even the most minute processes characteristic of soil and plant life will not be violated.

A range is never completely static; it is constantly moving either up or down in terms of range condition. Even though a properly managed range may be retained within limits of a rather static plane, there still will be those fluctuations of gains and losses in the soil-plant-air-water relationships that regulate forage production.

CHANGES IN THE GRAZING ASPECT OF RANGES

The range is a complex of plant communities. The most obvious indication of a plant community that denotes range, in contrast to other vegetation complexes, is the perennial availability of grazable forage. Before severe and continuous disturbance of the climax vegetation took place, plant communities were of four distinct categories: grass, forbs, shrubs, and forest. Each of these when considered individually dictated the use for which each kind of vegetation and land was best suited. From the beginning, range was a dominant land use, and it continues to be the only suitable use for vast areas, especially in the western hemisphere.

Through the years of domestic use of these lands, along with associated influences such as drought and cultural agriculture, once stable plant communities have too often become plant complexes, often of nondescript characteristics. Under the most severe conditions of change, there may be little or no resemblance to the original plant community. The most striking of such changes have been the transformation of open grasslands to brushy or wooded ranges, which now prevail on much of the rangeland of North America and South America. Such changes have become commonplace over much of the grassland or grassland and shrub associations and are literally taken for granted as the proper image for those ranges.

As a corollary to the frequent misconception of what a range should look like is the further lack of knowledge and understanding of its productive capacity. A further complication of the problem is the preconceived notion of grazing capacities that conform to historical records. Even authenticated reports give grazing capacities of ranges that were, at the time, over estimated. But these and other bits of information have been passed down through the years, and not without profound influence on the whole ranching industry.

The changed image of rangelands is nothing more than the combined total of many and varied indicators that have controlled trends in range condition. It is obvious that the most significant and striking indicators on any range are those having to do with grazing capacities and current overgrazing (Fig. 41). They emphasize the importance and the necessity for reevaluating the range and making adjustments in management and use. The important grazing plants, their abundance, and use, in contrast with other plants in the composition, reveal what is taking place on that range (Fig. 42).

Fig. 41. Current overgrazing of pasture on the left is a first indicator of a declining range condition and will result in decreased forage production next year.

Fig. 42. In contrast to Fig. 41, current use of this range in late winter is such that the range condition will be maintained or improved, and the grass will be in prime condition for maximum production the following spring.

In addition, these indicators of grazing values and use serve to point out annual variations in forage production, and permit the correlation of production with wet and dry years. Thus, they afford a basis for maintaining a proper balance between utilization and conservation of the range resource, and are important in developing and applying a range and ranch management plan.

INTERRELATION OF RANGE TRENDS AND RANGE CONDITION INDICATORS

It is difficult to consider range trends without at the same time taking into consideration range condition indicators. And it is nearly impossible to separate range trend indicators and range condition indicators and deal with one group individually without consideration of the other.

To the extent these are distinguishing characteristics of range trend indicators and range condition indicators, three basic concepts must be recognized: (1) Range trends are more or less concrete in substance, are visible evidence of changes that have taken place on the range, and they extend over a period of time usually representing several to many years. (2) Range condition indicators may be either concrete or abstract, signifying a condition; are rather current in development and subject to fluctuations; and may or may not persist over a period of time. (3) Range condition indicators are very often indicators of a range trend; that is, if allowed to persist, they very likely will become a concrete component of a range trend.

Because of this interrelationship, any discussion must be broadly interpreted to recognize the significance of the situation and deal with it in its proper perspective. In the following discussion, no attempt has been made to identify every development as to whether it be a range trend or a range condition indicator. The point is, appropriate treatment and management of any range development must be the criterion for either a range trend or range condition indicator. Indicators of a declining range condition may be reversed, thereby influencing or even changing a range trend. Or, treatment may alter a range trend, to be closely followed by indicators of either an improved or a declining range condition.

SIGNIFICANCE OF CLIMAX TO RANGE TRENDS AND RANGE CONDITION INDICATORS

If range trends are to be significant to range management, there must be a starting place as well as a destination. The climax for any site is the only real stable anchor there is in a dynamic realm of plant life. Therefore, it is a logical beginning from which any deviation, regardless of how small or how great, can be evaluated.

For purposes of this discussion, individual communities of grasses, forbs, shrubs, and trees do not necessarily represent a true climax unless the relationship of one to another and the influence of the environment are taken into account. A grass climax in one climate may be quite different from a grass climax in another climate. In like manner, a grass climax on one range site may differ from a grass climax on another range site within the same climate. This is because of differences in grasses and their environmental requirements. Such a situation is well illustrated by recognition of the true prairie, mixed prairie, and desert grassland (Figs. 43, 44, 45). Each of these has a

Fig. 43. A grass climax representative of the true prairie. Grasses include big bluestem, Indiangrass, switchgrass, little bluestem, sideoats grama, blue grama, and hairy grama. (Photo courtesy U.S. Soil Conservation Service, Texas.)

grass climax, but not of the same grasses. A more localized illustration might be a sandy land climax versus a mixed land climax side by side in any climate (Figs. 46 and 47).

Because of these variations, there are many combinations of plant communities that make up the equally numerous grass climaxes. Combinations of plant communities as grass and shrub communities are also found in association as a true climax for an area. Forest with communities of both undergrowth (shrubs) and grass provides a climax not commonly thought of as range; however, those lands are coming into range use throughout the forested areas of North America as well as in other parts of the world.

Of particular significance to the climax concept is the fact there is no "weed" climax, wherein weedy plants dominate the composition. This is logical from the standpoint of the common concept that a weed is any plant out of place. However, forbs, or weeds in common terminology, do have a place and a grazing value as a part of a plant community that is a true climax. These are recognized as climax forbs, just as there are climax shrubs and trees in many plant communities. Where these conditions occur, all climax plants are given equal importance in the range condition evaluation. In contrast, these weedy plants (forbs, shrubs, or trees) serve as perhaps the most readily recognized indicator of a downward trend in range condition when they move into a depleted climax. As they increase in abundance and in time dominate the site, their significance as an indicator of a downward trend is emphasized.

Fig. 44. Climax grasses of the mixed prairie include little bluestem, sideoats grama, blue grama, with some less important species such as hairy grama and buffalograss. On some sites there will be small amounts of sand bluestem and switchgrass. (Photo courtesy U.S. Soil Conservation Service, Texas.)

Fig. 45. A mountain range of the desert southwest with a near climax stand of grass including sideoats grama, black grama, and galleta. There are also small amounts of a perennial threeawn and hairy grama.

Fig. 46. A sandy land climax of bluestem grasses, Indiangrass, and switchgrass in Wheeler County, Texas (24-inch rainfall).

Fig. 47. In contrast to the sandy land climax of Wheeler County, Texas (Fig. 46) a nearby mixed land site supports a climax of some tall grasses along with short and mid-grasses, such as blue grama, sideoats grama, vine mesquite, and buffalograss. (Photo courtesy U.S. Soil Conservation Service, Texas.)

SIGNIFICANCE OF LOCAL GRAZING TYPES

Although the climax is a logical starting point for determining range trends and recognizing range indicators, it cannot be the universal criterion for practical management of a range. It does, however, serve as the objective for initiating treatment and management that will influence range trends. The climax is indicative of the comparative value of one kind of range relative to another. It also serves as the index to the identity of range indicators and the extent and direction of range trends. It is a basis for recognizing the various plant formations and compositions of a range site.

Although the climax is basic to any reliable range evaluation, the local and current groupings of plant communities determine the grazing capacity and the proper system of management for a particular range. Furthermore, such groupings must be recognized and reckoned with for each different kind of rangeland or range site. Usually this will result in a classification of few to many groupings of plant communities, sometimes within a single grazing unit or pasture.

The significance of local grouping of plant communities has led to the system of range site and range condition evaluations of rangeland. This concept was discussed fully in Chapter 5.

RANGE TRENDS AS INFLUENCED BY GRAZING

Aside from natural causes over which man has no control, such as drought, freezing temperatures, and accidental burns, grazing has the primary influence on range trends. Overgrazing is more significant in this respect than light or proper grazing, since overgrazing of range plants will normally be reflected by range indicators more quickly than will light grazing. In either instance, however, the balance is so exact that any significant disturbance can be readily detected by the interested and observant range manager. Because grazing itself is a rather severe disturbance, its effects upon growth, maintenance, and reproduction can be readily determined. When geared to the best plants in a composition, the relative use or nonuse of all other plants in that composition become distinct indicators of what is happening to that range.

The degree of grazing use of the better plants with respect to their essential growth requirements is of first importance. If the use made

of those plants is sufficiently light to insure the physiological requirements, under current environmental conditions, detrimental effects
will be nil, for all practical purposes. On the other hand, if grazing
use is more than it should be, the physiological requirements for
those better plants will be deficient. This is not the only penalty imposed on these better plants and the range. While they are being
taken by preference to the extent of being overgrazed to any degree,
other less desirable plants in the composition are provided an advantage. Water, plant food materials, and room not used by the
heavily used plants become available to enhance growth of those
secondary plants. Any system of grazing management that permits
any degree of overuse sets into motion competition between the desirable and less desirable plants. As already pointed out, the competition favors the less desirable plants, which is indicative of a
downward trend. Vigorous growth and reproduction of these plants
will be in evidence.

Indicators of this downward trend of the range resource will become increasingly evident and significant to range condition. In contrast, a range that has been subjected to grazing causing a downward
trend can be reversed and improved. By reverting to a proper degree
of grazing use of the best plants in the composition, an upward trend
in range condition can result. Obviously, with indicators of a downward trend already established, indicators of improvement will be
rather difficult to detect at first. A first indicator would be recognition of proper grazing use of the better plants of the composition.
(As a measure, proper use would be taking no more than 50 per cent,
by weight, of those better plants by the end of the grazing season.
This amount is of the current season of production under prevailing
conditions.)

Once a downward trend in range condition is halted and improvement is started, progress is extremely slow. However, as the range
condition improves, better plants will assert themselves in the composition, and improvement will be speeded up materially. With continued improvement, successive stages of the plant composition will
develop, ultimately again reaching climax for the site. It should be
noted, however, that with severe deterioration of range vegetation,
a corresponding depletion of the soil will usually occur. If this happens, it may prevent the return to the true and original climax. But
a climax for existing conditions will result.

INDICATORS OF A DOWNWARD TREND IN RANGE CONDITION

The first indicator of a downward trend in range condition is a degree of grazing in any one season that is heavier than that necessary to insure growth requirements of plants. Recognition of this condition requires a knowledge of the kinds of plants and what would constitute 50 per cent of current production. Too often these factual details are disguised by an abundance of secondary plants that are grazed little or not at all.

Overgrazing, as indicated by an excessive amount of the best range plants being taken, is the indicator about which something can be done. A step in the right direction can be achieved simply by not grazing choice plants in excess of the permissive 50 per cent of current production for the season. This is not to say that immediate response will result in a greatly increased production. Nor can the initial improvement be readily detected as something concrete at the outset. But in the very season that a plant is not grazed beyond its tolerable limit, there begins a buildup of available food supplies and other growth requirements. Several years may be required, if those plants are severely deteriorated, before measurable improvements are made. But an upward trend in range condition has been established, which is something to build on.

Of all indicators of a downward trend in range condition, recognition of overuse of the important plants is paramount. When management adjustments are geared to proper use of those plants, all other indicators of a downward trend and lowered range condition are being curtailed. It is not reasonable to expect well-established indicators of range deterioration to be overcome at once, since in all likelihood they have been developing over a period of years. That development must first be halted and then reversed to a process of improvement. First indications of such improvement will be in plant reaction to better treatment, making available more of its growth requirements.

Realistically, most ranges throughout the United States and other countries have a downward trend of condition and are continuing in that direction. Therefore, the opportunity of detecting the important indicators of range depletion in the very early stages is rather remote. However, the indicator of a degree of overuse is just as significant in lower stages of range condition as in the higher

Fig. 48. A low-condition range with strong indicators of a downward trend in evidence: only unpalatable grasses left ungrazed; only a few weak plants, heavily grazed, of the better grasses; much bare ground; encroachment of mesquite and cactus. (Photo courtesy U.S. Soil Conservation Service, Texas.)

stages. In either instance, overuse of the best plants for that condition, whatever they are, must be alleviated if a downward trend is to be reversed to insure range improvement.

With a continued downward trend in range condition, indicators become progressively more pronounced and more abundant. Although specific indicators or the intensity of their occurrence do not apply to all rangelands alike, the same kinds of indicators are generally applicable to all rangelands (Figs. 48 and 49). Therefore, they can be discussed in general with specific applications made according to the kind of rangeland and its environment.

Fig. 49. On deep sandy land ranges of the southern plains, the encroachment of shinnery oak is a very definite indicator of a downward trend in range condition. (Photo courtesy U.S. Soil Conservation Service, Texas.)

In addition to the primary evidence of range overuse, other indicators of a downward trend, generally in their order of occurrence, are:

1. Weakened condition and lowered vigor of better plants. Indications of this condition are fewer stems and shorter leaves; very early development of seed stems with few or no foliage stems; shorter stems and decreased volume of forage and total forage production (Fig. 50).

2. Decrease in size and abundance of the better plants. These plants begin to decrease in size and ground cover; turf grasses

Fig. 50. A blue grama range with weakened plants, few short stems, all with seed heads, no foliage stems, and few short leaves is a sure indication of downward trend in range condition.

Fig. 51. A currently overused range that evidences how perennial bunch grasses are thinning out. Annual grasses and weeds are occupying the area from which the better grass has disappeared. (Photo courtesy U.S. Soil Conservation Service, Texas.)

Fig. 52. This range once supported a 75 to 80 per cent stand of blue grama. With deterioration in past years, buffalograss, a strong increaser, now forms 60 per cent of the total grass cover.

begin to thin and open the stand; bunch grasses show signs of dying out, giving way to less desirable increaser grasses, weeds, and eventually bare ground. Current overuse of a range only emphasizes this downward trend (Fig. 51).

3. Appearance of invading plants. Continued decline of better grass plants results in more bare ground releasing more plant food and water in excess of that which a weakened stand of good plants can use; less desirable plants of the climax increase in size and number; plants not a part of the climax appear to occupy bare areas and use excess food and water not required by deteriorated climax plants; usually first invaders are high-type annual plants furnishing some grazing use.

4. Subdominance of climax plants. Grazable increaser plants and palatable invaders become dominant in the composition (Fig. 52). Perennial forbs, half-shrubs and shrubs may become invaders. Unpalatable plants of all plant groups appear. The ranching operation is becoming dependent on the production

Fig. 53. A depleted range seldom produces more than depleted live-stock. Ranching out of the feed bag to supplement these conditions is costly.

Fig. 54. Creosotebush has dominated this desert grassland range. Control of the brush is necessary before a grass stand can be successfully reestablished.

Fig. 55. Once an open grassland, this range has been near completely dominated by brush. In this area of south Texas, excellent stands of grass can be reestablished with brush removal.

and quality of secondary plants. Short-lived annuals, forbs, and grasses become prevalent with fluctuating rainfall. These may be either summer or winter annuals, such as annual brome grasses, plantains, and others adapted to a climate.

5. Livestock production. Early stages of range deterioration may or may not be reflected in livestock production. With continued decline in range condition, however, a reduction in range forage production and thus livestock production follows closely (Fig. 53). Usually supplemental feed and minerals are important, if not required, with continued range deterioration. A common indicator occurrence that affects and coincides with livestock production is the invasion of poisonous plants. And, increased grazing of unpalatable plants is a sure indicator of a downward trend in range condition.

6. Dominance of woody plants. Where woody species are adapted and there is a source, they eventually dominate a deteriorating

Fig. 56. A badly depleted and eroded range becomes less productive each year. Here the grass cover is insufficient to prevent serious sheet and gully erosion. (Photo courtesy U.S. Soil Conservation Service, Texas.)

range condition. This dominance very rapidly destroys range forage plants by competitive use of practically all plant growth requirements (space, soil, plant food, water, sunlight, and air). Woody species will become firmly established to the extent of being recognized as a post-climax. Under these conditions, management alone will have little if any effect on improving such a range. Examples of this phenomenon are creosote-tarbush ranges of the southwest, brushy ranges of south Texas, shinnery oak-sand sage complexes of the southern plains (Figs. 54 and 55).

7. Deterioration of soil. Climax ranges are found only on climax soils that are productive and stable (immature sandyland soils are an exception as to stability). As range deterioration progresses, soil disturbance and deterioration follows. Evidence of soil deterioration includes surface erosion, rilling, gully formation, loss of organic content, compaction, reduced air and water intake with increased run-off, and unhealthy and unproductive soil conditions in general (Fig. 56).

INDICATORS OF AN UPWARD TREND IN RANGE CONDITION

Indicators of an upward trend in range condition are as important to range management as those reflecting a downward trend. They occur in the same general areas of plant and soil reactions. And they are, for the most part, a contrast of conditions and reactions to those indicating a downward trend.

Just as recognition of overgrazing the better plants of current production indicates a downward trend, recognition of proper use or even underuse denotes an upward trend. The relationship of degrees of grazing to trends in range condition, as discussed in the previous section on downward trends, is also applicable to any consideration of upward trends.

In addition to the current use factor as an indicator of range condition trend, there are other indicators of trends of range improvement. Although many such indicators are not yet recognized over various kinds of range, the following apply to ranges in general:

1. Health and vigor of important plants. Improved health and vigor of the better forage plants may follow a proper degree of grazing use by one to several years. It would be increasingly evident by such indicators of improved range condition as an increase in plant development and volume of growth; an increase in numbers of stems; increased height of stems and length of leaves; an increased proportion of vegetative stems to seed stems in early stages of plant growth; seed stem development being delayed until near the mid-point of the current growing season.

2. Degree of grazing use of the range as a whole. Use, but not over use, of the better grazing plants (grass plants are better maintained in a productive state by being properly grazed than by a complete nonuse); secondary plants grazed light to moderate; invader grasses, forbs, and shrubs grazed lightly, primarily to satisfy animal needs for variety in the diet; no evidence of hedging shrub and tree growth; with proper grazing use of the best plants, all other plants, increasers and invaders alike, will respond with increased vigor and production (a natural response, but with continued good management these plants will not dominate the site); on brushy ranges or ranges with tree

growth previously overused, as indicated by hedging, conspicu-
ous signs of browsing will begin to disappear (Fig. 57); no grazing of poisonous or otherwise noxious plants.

3. Plant succession. The appearance of young plants of the better
grasses and desirable forbs is the most accurate indication of
proper management of the range. These plants may be slow in
starting but will improve the composition quite rapidly once
they begin to appear. New plants may develop as seedlings,
tillers, or even from crown buds from latent or severely dwarfed
old plant remains. New plants of invading species should not
be interpreted as an indicator of an upward trend in range condition.

4. Stability and improved soil conditions. Soil erosion scars begin
to heal over with vegetation (Fig. 58). With severe erosion, sheet
or gully, the establishment of any form of plant growth is indicative of improvement (erosion control by natural recovery
of vegetation has limitations beyond which erosion control
measures become necessary). Soil compaction becomes less
severe with better tilth and increased rate of water intake. An
abundance of soil organisms near the surface is in evidence and
worm casts signify adequate worm activity near the surface.

5. Litter accumulation. Litter from unused plant growth begins
to accumulate on the soil surface (Fig. 59). Once started, litter
accumulation and litter decomposition should nearly balance
on a properly managed range. As a precaution, excessive accumulation on ranges in high rainfall areas, or even by excessive amounts of unused secondary plants as a result of proper
grazing use, may actually be detrimental to range improvement.
It will exclude both air and sunlight. (Greater emphasis on the
practice of seasonal use is a most likely solution to this problem).

6. Plant composition and plant associations. In the ultimate
stages of range improvement, composition of the vegetation
and the arrangement of plant communities become important.
When climax grasses dominate, they arrange themselves in patterns of compatability that indicate the higher conditions of a
range. Tall-grass ranges of the true prairie have a tendency to
colonize. Big or sand bluestem, Indiangrass, and switchgrass

Fig. 57. An improved stand of grass on a brushy range with planned brush control is an indicator of an upward trend in range condition. Here goats are used and properly managed to aid in brush control. (Photo courtesy U.S. Soil Conservation Service, Texas.)

Fig. 58. Runoff and erosion have seriously depleted this valley site. The downward trend is being checked by an improved and maintained vegetative cover. (Photo courtesy U.S. Soil Conservation Service, Texas.)

Fig. 59. The accumulation of litter, especially that resulting from the unused portion of the better grasses, is a strong indicator of a proper degree of grazing and improvement of the range. (Photo courtesy U.S. Soil Conservation Service, Texas.)

Fig. 60. Note the groundcover of this heavily used, low-condition, blue grama-buffalograss range. (Photo courtesy U.S. Soil Conservation Service, Texas.)

Fig. 61. As a blue grama-buffalograss range improves, the stand will thin out by the buffalograss, an increaser, giving way to the more aggressive blue grama. (Photo courtesy U.S. Soil Conservation Service, Texas.)

form colonies, usually circular, with little bluestem filling in the areas between. As blue grama, and other short and mid-bunch grasses approach climax, the stand will very likely decrease from what it was in lower range condition (Figs. 60 and 61). There will be more interstices or bare ground between plants than when increaser and invader plants were abundant in the lower range condition. As climax is approached, plant spacing and plant population will adjust to the capability of the environment. This adjustment insures maximum development of root systems that will compete with invading plants, thus controlling weeds and even woody plants not already established on the site.

7. Livestock production indicative of range condition. With a progressive upward trend in range condition, livestock production will gradually improve also. To be substantially indicative, such improvement would be over a period of several years. Otherwise such increases may be a result of a temporary flush season of forage production, possibly including short-lived annual invaders. Increased livestock production must be tempered with reliable plant indicators, as described above.

RANGE TRENDS AND NORMAL PLANT REACTIONS

To the close observer, some natural plant reactions might be interpreted as an indicator of a downward trend in range condition. For example, the dying out and opening up in the center of the crown of bunch grasses may be an indication of range deterioration, or it might be a normal plant reaction. When this condition occurs in such grasses as blue grama, little bluestem, or the threeawns, other factors must be considered to make an accurate determination as to the cause. Certainly with a downward trend in condition of a range, having these and other bunch grasses, the dying out process takes place in an effort to adjust plant development to the available plant food supply. With further deterioration, the remaining outer ring of the plant crown begins to break down into very small individual plants (Fig. 62). By this process a range may actually increase in groundcover (density) of a choice grass. Other factors that then become highly significant are vigor of those plants, total production of forage, invading plants, and eventually whether those plants stay or go out of the composition.

Although this reaction of plant crown deterioration is very often a result of mismanagement, these same plants may react in this manner as a natural process of their life cycle. The initial development of a plant is at the point that eventually becomes the center of the crown. Here the first and therefore, over a period of time, the most bud formation and stem development take place. Of course, this area becomes congested with root and stem accumulation. Eventually, especially in drier climates, the congested condition leaves little room for new shoots. With no new shoots developing, an open crown results. This condition is more prevalent with unused plants than where such accumulations are prevented by grazing and trampling. Observations indicate that this process of dying out of grasses for reasons other than overgrazing will be noticeable within seven or eight years in the life cycle of the plant, even with what is considered good grazing management.

That this same process of plant reaction will occur regardless of how the plant is grazed might seem to indicate that there is little if anything to be gained from good management. Such a conclusion is totally unfounded, if for no other reason than that the stamina of the overused plants will not permit them to withstand all the many adversities of a deteriorating range. On the other hand, with proper

Fig. 62. Center crown breakdown of a bunch grass may be an indicator of range deterioration, or it may be a natural process of plant behavior. Here, range deterioration is indicated.

or even under use of a range, those plants which naturally progress through reactions of plant community development, including both constructive and destructive processes, will remain in the stand indefinitely. Furthermore, they will remain in the correct proportions as to species, and be properly distributed as far as the environment of that range is concerned.

Another normal plant reaction that might be interpreted as range deterioration is a comparatively low forage production but possibly a normal seed production. Such a condition is due to abnormal growing conditions, even with a high condition or an improving range. A normal reaction to such a range may be a direct result of poor distribution of rainfall. A lack of adequate moisture in the fall cuts down on plant food manufacture, storage, and subsequent bud formation for the next spring growth. This alone not only retards spring development of those plants the following year, but usually reduces total forage yield. Likewise, inadequate spring moisture for early growth will also reduce forage yields. If moisture is not available by the middle of the growing season, yields may be reduced to no more than 25 per cent of normal, regardless of the amount of delayed moisture. This is contrary to the concept that moisture at any time that allows plants to grow and make seed is sufficient. The difference is pounds of grass when only a seed crop is produced as compared to an early crop of forage, vegetative stems, and leaves.

Chapter 7

THE KEY RANGE SITE AND KEY SPECIES IN MANAGEMENT

Principles of management on open ranges. Grazing habits and preferences of grazing animals as indicative of the key range site and key species. Importance of characteristics of the key site and key species in judging utilization of a range. Change of the key site and the key species with significant changes in range condition. Good range management and productive use of all range sites in a pasture.

Considering the forage producing characteristics of various range sites and the many varied grazing habits and preferences of livestock, site selection by grazing animals is a significant basis for management. During the days of open range ranching, grazing habits and a natural instinct for the best quality of forage available to meet body needs provided the only basic principle of good range management. Fortunately, a good job was done until overcrowded conditions resulted from too many livestock and a quest for available water. Thereafter, land ownership and property boundaries began to restrict livestock movement over the range. This resulted in forced utilization of some sites and some forage plants, other than those that normally would have been a first choice.

Although restricted management imposed some limitations on both the range and the livestock, it did place a value on various range sites and range plants. Unfortunately, these values were not recognized as range trends and indicators of range condition until much of the country had deteriorated, often to a very low range condition. Perhaps the first shocking evidence of significant range deterioration was the serious decline of the more desirable range sites. It was those areas that first began to lose the better forage plants. Less desirable grasses, weeds, and brush began to appear, and eventually erosion and other marks of deterioration became a reality. Such a condition was the first indication of the necessity for concrete concern for the care and management of grazing lands.

GRAZING HABITS AND PREFERENCES

Inasmuch as the manipulation of livestock is the principal tool with which range management can be achieved, their grazing habits and preferences become the criteria for evaluating range use. These habits and preferences are reflected by the kind of livestock that will use various kinds of range, the degree to which they will graze various range plants, the extent to which they will graze over the entire range, and the season(s) that various range sites and range plants will be grazed. Thus, the four cardinal principles of range management are: the degree of grazing, the distribution of grazing, the season of grazing, and the kind of livestock best suited to the range.

Various kinds of livestock have distinct preferences as to the kind of forage best suited to their needs. These preferences, although overlapping to a considerable degree, usually coincide distinctly with kinds of rangeland, range sites, and range condition.

As a general guide to the grazing preference of range livestock, cattle will take, by choice, approximately 70 per cent of their diet from palatable grasses and 30 per cent from browse plants and forbs (Fig. 63). Horses have a little more preference for grass, taking about 90 per cent, when available, with only 10 per cent from browse and the forb category. Sheep will, by choice, take about 60 per cent of their diet from the better grasses and 40 per cent from other plants, with a slight preference for palatable forbs over browse plants (Fig. 64). Goats, being the most rugged grazers of all domestic livestock, have a preference for browse plants, taking approximately 60 per cent in their diet when available; the other 40 per cent is primarily from palatable grasses, and, of course, they do select some of the better forbs that may be available (Fig. 65).

This information is based primarily on observation of animals grazing and further substantiated by analysis of the pattern of grazed vegetation.[1]

---

[1] Volny M. Douglas, *Field Studies on Range Forage Utilization*, USDA Soil Conservation Service, Texas, 1942.

Fig. 63. Cattle have a strong preference for grass. There should be a choice as to the kind of livestock best suited to this range. (Photo courtesy U.S. Soil Conservation Service, Texas.)

Fig. 64. This range, with unpalatable brush cleared, produces good amounts of grass, browse, and forbs. The latter are available mostly in the spring and fall. This combination of forage makes an excellent range for sheep. (Photo courtesy U.S. Soil Conservation Service, Texas.)

Fig. 65. The browse line on the brush as high as can be reached by goats indicates their preference for this kind of forage. Note also that grass and forbs have been grazed in this pasture. (Photo courtesy U.S. Soil Conservation Service, Texas.)

When the natural first-choice kind of grazing land for a kind of livestock is available within a grazing unit, that will be the preference grazing area. When that natural choice is not available, another kind will be selected that most nearly meets their grazing requirements. This choice then becomes significant to the management and utilization of that range. Where a kind of livestock grazes first and the most throughout the grazing period (season or yearlong) is indicative of the key range site to management of the entire range. It will be the site grazed the hardest and the one that will deteriorate most rapidly without the support of the basic principles of range management.

There will be one or possibly two forage plants on this site that are a first choice for grazing over any other plants. Those plants are usually of first importance to the livestock grazing that range. However, the principles of choice may be discarded for short periods, owing to seasonal palatability of other plants, either on that site or some other accessible site.

The range management objective in recognizing a key grazing site with one and not more than two key plants is to have a unit of measure as to the use of the entire pasture or range. The principle of use is the fact that if the most favored range site within a pasture is not overgrazed, neither will any other site in the pasture be over-grazed. When the better or key site is cared for, all other sites will care for themselves.

CHARACTERISTICS OF A KEY RANGE SITE

It is a fallacy to judge the key range site solely on the basis of live-stock preference. Such factors as range condition, location, or terrain might unduly influence livestock grazing preference. But even so, the basic resources of a site may be of such potential as to insure it being the key to management and use of that range. Furthermore, it may be necessary to identify the key site to a management unit at a time when it is not being grazed. For these reasons it is important to recognize criteria by which a key site may logically be identified.

Of first importance is the kind of plants that are there now. If these are not the best plants that will grow there, what will be there under good management? Choice grazing plants would be palatable and nutritious throughout most or all of the grazing period. They would be high yielding and preferred by the kind of animals that will graze the range. The relative abundance of the choice species should be sufficient to carry the major portion of the grazing load. And, they should be strong enough to compete with other plants growing on the site, under grazing conditions.

The size of the key site is important to management because of the distribution of grazing factor. Ordinarily, the key site should be at least 25 per cent of the total area of the grazing unit or pasture. This may be a single site area, or it may be the sum of two or more areas of that site within the grazing unit. The smaller the area of the key site, the greater the concentration of grazing. Thus, greater will be the effects of trampling and wastage of forage. A possible exception in favor of a smaller site would be one of extremely high production in comparison to other sites in the unit. An example is a wet bottomland site or meadow, but even there, effects would be felt from a concentration of livestock.

To be a key site, the area would be far enough removed from points of livestock concentration that it would not be affected by pressure grazing. A site near a water location, in close proximity to a head-quarters or in travel-ways, should never be considered a key site. Such areas receive too much repeat grazing and trampling disturbance to represent normal grazing use.

The key site must be one that will, by choice, be grazed through at least most of the grazing period (season or yearlong). That means it must be readily accessible, a terrain that allows for ease of grazing, and one that provides quality forage throughout the greater portion of the grazing period.

These characteristics, along with a reasonable knowledge of live-stock grazing habits and preferences, provide a practical basis for management decisions.

CHARACTERISTICS OF KEY SPECIES

Along with the key range site, a single forage species will usually be more attractive than any other to the livestock using the range. In addition to the quality of the forage of a key site, as discussed above, there are characteristics of an individual species that make it also a key to management and use of the range.

The first consideration is the identity of the best climax decreaser, of high quality, growing on the key site. It also should be important to the potential of the site and one that will respond to management. It must be in sufficient quantity, at least 20 per cent of the available forage, and readily accessible to alleviate pressure grazing. And, it must be vigorous enough to insure normal plant development.

When a single species of a climax decreaser with the above char-acteristics is not available, then the species with next highest qualities should be considered. Quite often a logical choice may include two or three climax decreasers with similar site responses. In addition to the qualities of a single species, as described above, additional factors should be considered: the species most important to the potential of the site, the comparative length of the season of palatability, normal grazing preference by the kind of livestock that will be using the range, a comparative degree of plant utilization through normal grazing, and plant response to grazing.

If there is no climax decreaser currently growing on the key site in sufficient quantity to be a key species, a good increaser species may be a next choice. To be a reliable key species, it should have the qualities of a decreaser species, to the fullest possible extent. In addition, it should have a season of palatability commensurate with the length of the planned grazing season (the grazing season may need to be adjusted accordingly). It must be compatible in adjusting to an improved range condition with decreaser plants. This means it will not be a species that will dominate the site by agressive seeding or vegetative reproduction. For this reason, some species of threeawn (Aristida) and tobosagrass are objectionable as key plants in some localities.

In some instances, neither a climax decreaser nor a suitable increaser species is available to be designated the key species for management and use decisions. Such conditions generally preclude grazing use other than seasonal grazing when invading plants will furnish suitable forage. However, even under these conditions, recognition should be given to a proper degree of grazing. Usually there will be one perennial plant that has invaded the range and which has a semblance of grazing quality. This quality may be a result of forced utilization, but it does represent a degree of grazing. Such a plant may be used as a temporary key to grazing management. That is to say, by not overgrazing an inferior plant, if it is the best plant on the range, there can be some progress toward an improved condition. Such progress may be limited to an accumulation of litter and a retarding of runoff and erosion. That, in turn, can add water, an essential growth requirement of any plant of a little higher quality that may be struggling for existence.

On any grazing land in the range category, there will be a plant, or group of plants, that will provide guidance to management and grazing use.

KEY RANGE SITES AND KEY SPECIES WILL CHANGE

When rangeland is in or near climax condition, the key site and key species are selected from among those that are superior in grazing value. Thus, the true grazing value of each site is indicated by how much, when, and for how long it will be selectively grazed. Likewise, with these conditions, various sites as well as the range as a whole can be reasonably well evaluated by livestock production.

Under these conditions of near climax, it is not difficult to identify key grazing areas both as to the site and species. Grazing pressure can be much more readily recognized when it occurs. Furthermore, the overall grazing resource is much more stable, permitting needed adjustments in grazing management. Also, under stable conditions of a high-condition range, production is much more predictable. The ranching operation is less dependent on the necessity for seasonal rainfall and seasonal production of "catch crop" types of forage production.

A decline in range condition means that the composition of the vegetation is changing. The process of retrogression is taking place. Since the key site is preferred most by the livestock, if overgrazing is permitted, it will be the first site of that grazing unit to decline in condition. Because of its preference, the further down the scale it declines, the harder it is grazed. Animals will continue to seek the last morsel of the best grass adapted to that site. Eventually, however, those best grasses will have been replaced by plants, grasses, or possibly forbs, that are less palatable and nutritious and which will have less preference. As this process continues, some species on another site may become the most desirable plant in the pasture—not that it is as desirable as the original key species and its corresponding key site, but because it is the best there is. These then become the key site and key species.

It is also possible to improve a range to the point at which more desirable plants become prevalent and are the key species and, where they are found, the key site.

USING KEY SITES AND KEY SPECIES TO JUDGE RANGE USE

When the key range site and the key species have been determined for a grazing unit, they then become the barometer for range management. The range manager has only to observe what is taking place on that site and the degree of use that is made of the key species. As a general rule, livestock will spend some time on the key range site almost every day. However, there will be seasons when they may abandon the key site almost completely in favor of some other seasonable palatable site and species. Animals are also apt to leave the key site almost every day in search of a variety of forage to mix and balance their diet. But almost without exception, they will return to the key site, often to the extent of abusive use of it if appropriate management is not applied. It is the response to use of the key site that dictates the need for adjustments in management. This has proven to be the most reliable guide to range management available to the ranch operator. Not only is it reliable but convenient, easily read, and easily interpreted. To the good ranch operator who is knowledgeable of not only his livestock but also his range, the condition and use of the key range site are reflected in the condition of his livestock. When their condition and the current degree of use on the key range site are both satisfactory, the management of that grazing unit can be considered satisfactory.

GETTING PRODUCTIVE USE OF ALL RANGE SITES

A logical question to the foregoing discussion is whether judging the degree of grazing on the first preference site only will allow full utilization of the entire pasture or range. It will, but not without management of the entire grazing unit. If livestock, by choice, spend 75 per cent of their time (the year) on the key grazing site, then the annual stocking rate should be based primarily on the amount of forage produced on that site. A common fallacy in the ranching business is to stock a pasture on the basis of the total acreage, allowing so many acres to the animal. Then, by choice, the entire herd spends the greater part of the grazing season or year on perhaps 25 per cent or less of the pasture, which is usually the key site to management. Needless to say, that area is more than likely abusively grazed (Fig. 66).

In almost any grazing unit, or pasture, some sites will be secondary to the key site, but they provide a significant amount of forage. Such forage also is secondary to that produced on the key site, or it too would be a key site. It may be palatable only during a particular short season. It may be coarse and harsh except in very early stages of growth. Or, it may not be easily accessible, resulting in limited grazing use.

Sites with characteristics such as these require individual attention to get the most from them without adversely affecting some part of the range. Such attention requires a knowledge of the kind of forage plants, the time they will be grazed by choice, and the kind of livestock that will make best use of them. In addition, the need for sea-

Fig. 66. This valley site is only a very small per cent of the pasture, but livestock spend probably 75 per cent of their total time grazing this area. (Photo courtesy U.S. Soil Conservation Service, Texas.)

sonal adjustments in stocking rates must be recognized. Adjustments needed may be an increase or a decrease in numbers and possibly in kinds or classes of animals. The period of adjustment may last for only a few weeks, or for the entire season. Nevertheless, adjustments should be geared to the situation on the range and not to a pattern of convenience or calendar dates.

To emphasize the principles of grazing management in order to obtain efficient use from comparatively inferior range sites, note the following examples. It has been noted that in the Edwards Plateau of Texas, sheep will, in the fall, leave palatable grasses in valleys and swales and graze hairy tridens on shallow rocky hills and ridges. In the southwest, some species of threeawn will be grazed by preference, because of its early emergence in the spring. Tobosa grass, having a very short season of palatability, will be readily grazed in early spring and, with moisture, even into the summer; thereafter it becomes coarse and unpalatable. Numerous forbs and browse plants have seasonal periods of high palatability and nutritive quality.

With these conditions and resources on a ranch, the good range manager will use this type of forage when it is most usable. When in sufficient quantities, it is often desirable to concentrate the grazing on these areas of less-desirable forage for brief periods when those plants are palatable. That is, stock the pasture or range at a heavy rate to insure proper or perhaps overuse of the particular forage in question. To do so will accomplish two profitable objectives. First, otherwise wasted forage will be converted into beef or other livestock products; and second, excessive growth and competition of those less desirable plants with the better plants that should be improved will be eliminated. A word of caution: This heavy grazing load should never extend beyond the period of palatability of the particular plants being heavily grazed. To allow it to do so immediately results in overuse of the desirable plants in that composition. This has been the fate of most ranges where such grasses as tobosa, galleta, threeawn, some of the dropseeds, and others have become established as the dominant vegetation on many sites.

The more widely variable range sites there are in a pasture, the more intricate the grazing pattern will be. It becomes more difficult to correlate the season and the length of time a particular site will be used. Under such conditions, a system of rotation grazing or rotation deferment is most appropriate, as will be discussed later.

Under these varied conditions, the key site actually becomes less significant, but greater importance must be given a key grazing species. There may be one, or possibly two, desirable species distributed over sites other than the key site. They will actually carry the bulk of the grazing load throughout the grazing season or year. Blue grama and black grama are examples of this situation, often on large areas of southwest ranges. Little bluestem can also be identified in the same manner in the mixed prairie country and sometimes in the true prairie when the range condition has declined from the climax.

Chapter 8

RANGE UTILIZATION

Minimizing some sacrifice areas. Utilization based on choice plants of the range. More accurate evaluations through early procedures in judging range utilization. Utilization of ranges, along with seasonal characteristics of range use. Knowledge of utilization at any time of the year—a key to productive management. Rancher evaluation of utilization as a basis for management judgments. Utilization checks on poor condition ranges. Significance of checks of both warm season and cool season plants.

Proper utilization of range forage is important to both range management and livestock production. The way individual plants are used results in the range being maintained, depleted, or improved. Furthermore, utilization of range forage is reflected in production from the animals that use the range.

On any range, or any individual range site, utilization may vary from no use to complete use of all grazable plants. In range terminology these degrees of use are referred to as "proper use," "over use," or "under use." Stoddart and Smith, in their text on range management, define range utilization as "the degree to which animals have consumed the total current production of a range area; it is expressed in percentage by weight."

From the management standpoint, it is not enough to judge range utilization on the basis of an overall aspect, that is, with the exception of when all, or practically all, grazable plants have been near completely used. Such conditions can be interpreted only as an over used range. Otherwise the crux to the utilization of the range must be reconciled with the more important forage plants. It is these plants and their recurrent treatment through grazing use that will regulate the response and trend of the range to a higher or lower condition. This is not to say that these important plants alone can be used on well managed ranges, but that it is only through proper use of the better plants that ranges can be maintained or improved. To achieve this objective requires something less than what might be proper use of secondary plants in the composition. Very often such overall use of a range may actually result in what appears to be a wastage of grass. Although this may be a factor in some instances, it generally can be overcome through range use practices. This is especially true where pastures are not too large for the type of operation involved, and where manipulation of livestock is feasible. On large year long ranges, such practices as distribution of water and salt may be quite effective in achieving better distribution of grazing and proper utilization of all forage. Otherwise, proper utilization may be achieved only through adjusting the stocking rate to what would result in no more than a proper degree of utilization of the more important plants of the range.

SACRIFICES IN RANGE UTILIZATION

From the practical point of view, it is not possible to achieve proper utilization of each and every parcel of range on any ranch. There will always be those areas of concentration where grazing use will be heavier than it should be for good management. Locales around water and salt locations and near headquarters are examples of unavoidable over use under most any system of management (Fig. 67). Also, owing to location, quality of the forage, or ease of grazing, some sites may have a special preference to livestock, resulting in selective grazing of that area. Frequently these sites are too small to use as a basis for management of the pasture.

Areas that must be over-utilized to get proper use on the majority of the range are recognized as "sacrifice areas." More than likely they are characterized by a total lack of the kind of forage plants that should be there. And, in too many instances, these areas are the most productive land on the ranch, as in the case of narrow valley or bottomland sites.

Although good management and proper utilization of such areas are difficult under most any practical management plan, beneficial treatment is not out of the question. Any system of rotation grazing will allow some relief from over utilization—perhaps not enough for complete recovery, but beneficial improvements can be had. When benefits are not sufficient under grazing management best suited to

Fig. 67. Water locations and bedgrounds are sacrifice areas, regardless of how good the management program may be.

the pasture as a whole, periodic complete rest through a full growing season may be justified. Such decisions would have to be made by the rancher when all factors of the ranch operation are weighed and evaluated. Of most importance is having a minimum of these areas on any ranch.

CHOICE OF PLANTS TO BE MANAGED

An important range management consideration that results from forage utilization is the kinds of plants to be maintained on the range. With the degree of utilization being the regulatory factor as to the way plants react, that then is the technique by which kinds of plants in the composition can be controlled.

There may be instances when a very desirable plant of the climax is only minor in the composition. Thus, managing for the improvement or even the maintenance of that species may be impractical commensurate with total forage production. Therefore, the man-

Fig. 68. Texas wintergrass (Stipa leucotricha) has moved from the gulf coast northward, providing excellent grazing on some sites in central and west central Texas.

agement objective would be the maintenance of other species in the composition that would be equally satisfactory as forage for that range. Achievement of this objective would be realized through controlled utilization of the plants to be maintained.

Also, there may be instances where a high-quality, climax species may not be any more productive or suitable for grazing than a secondary species. In fact, a secondary species may be more easily managed and have grazing qualities more suitable to the rancher's wishes. He may therefore select the secondary species as his management objective. Texas wintergrass, (*stipa leucotricha*), as it has moved northward into various kinds of ranges from the gulf coast to central west Texas and the rolling plains, is a secondary grass that may well be a choice for management (Fig. 68).

EARLY PROCEDURES IN JUDGING RANGE UTILIZATION

The earliest consideration of range utilization was the observation and judgment of the rancher. Experience was quickly gained as to how much current production had been grazed as of a given time. His judgment also dictated how much forage was left for use until a new production could be expected. These determinations were generally reasonably accurate in terms of total forage production.

Although forage production and consumption determinations were made with a high degree of accuracy, that was not enough to fulfill the requirements of good range management. Requirements of plants for maintenance in the stand and grazing habits of animals were not taken into account. Growth requirements of plants, includ ing food manufacturing processes, food storage, root development, crown-bud formation, room to grow, and competition were among the requirements not taken into account. Also, selectivity of the better plants, repeat grazing, closeness of grazing, seasonal palatability, and other grazing habits had a material effect on plant production and maintenance. These were not given consideration by even a most accurate evaluation of production and harvest of range forage. These deficiencies in judgment contributed to range deterioration in the early days of the ranching industry.

Very early in the history of the United States Forest Service, forest rangers became aware of what was taking place. Steps were taken to correct undisputed evidence of serious and rapid range depletion. Their efforts were continued and in fact greatly enhanced through scientific investigations of the correlation between plant growth requirements and the grazing of various kinds of animals. These investigations are continuing through the efforts of plant scientists representing various agencies, institutions, and private foundations and endowments throughout the world. Procedures have been developed and perfected to a high degree of accuracy. Precision techniques are at the disposal of the scientist, while more practical evaluations have been and are being developed for use of managers of rangelands.

Among the first ideas for judging the degree of use of range plants was to use the height of the grazed plant, or stubble, as a basis. Such a basis merely took into account the average growth height of various species in the composition. To this average plant development could be compared the average stubble height after grazing. The difference could readily be converted to percentage, which was indicative of the degree of utilization of the range. At the beginning, effort was made to determine these percentages for most or perhaps all plants that were being grazed. For a range area, or the range as a whole, if reasonably uniform, a composite percentage figure could be arrived at which was a measure of the degree of range use.

Following the height concept for judging range utilization came the weight measure. This procedure embodied volume, but it was not included in the degree of use determination at the outset. However, volume very soon became a significant factor when correlated with height and weight of grazed plants in contrast to ungrazed plants of the same species. Logically, key plants for grazing were determined to be most reliable for use determinations, since they are used first and most under any system of management.

All these procedures have been developed, refined, and put into use through the years of scientific developments in the field of plant science. Without exception, every detail of these developments has contributed to the broad scope of range management. Of particular significance is the attention focused on the individual species, and, in fact, the individual plant within the species. This was important not only from the standpoint of utilization but from the standpoint of plant response to grazing and its relationship to other plants on that range.

HOW RANGES ARE UTILIZED

With experience in the procedures discussed above, and in more recent range investigations, the importance of individual species in the grazing pattern becomes more significant. This significance prevails whether there is a wide diversity of range plants or a homogeneous type of range site.

Grazing animals select plants that more nearly satisfy their needs and likes at the moment. Regardless of the quality of plants at hand, they will select one or possibly two or three plants and graze them more than any other. This does not mean that no other plants will be grazed at that time, since some secondary plants will be taken for variety. When choice plants occur only in small quantities, other plants will be taken to the full extent necessary to satisfy animal needs.

This pattern of grazing does not necessarily continue throughout a grazing season. Plants may change in palatability or nutritive value with seasonal development. The coarseness or toughness of some plants may make them less desirable for grazing. These and possibly other variations in range forage will alter the grazing pattern of animals using the range. Because of these variations it is necessary that the range manager be able to interpret significant plant responses to grazing. This is necessary not only at the time grazing occurs but for any projected response during the current forage production season. Without such knowledge on which to base needed adjustments in grazing, over utilization and a downward trend in range condition is inevitable.

It is through a knowledge of plant reaction to grazing and grazing preferences, coupled with climatic influences, that the range manager can make use of range utilization information in management. Of first importance is recognition of the plants that are significantly abundant to carry an appreciable part of the grazing load. These must be plants that are a high choice for grazing over a considerable portion of the grazing season. Generally, plant groups with these characteristics are few in number on most any range. Ordinarily a single species can be identified, and seldom will there be more than two or three such quality species in a composition. If there are two or more such species, any one or all of them may be used in judging utilization, but making a judgment under such circumstances becomes more complex. In essence, all plants of each of the two or more species should be taken into account, but this condition seldom occurs.

Ideally, a single species is identified as being most representative of the production and use of the range. That species then becomes the key to management and use of that range. By continued observation of it through the grazing season, an intelligent interpretation of utilization and the remaining forage can be made. Also, it will be possible to interpret and predict the response of that range to current use and to subsequent use during the entire production and use period.

Recognition of preference grazing will identify not only the key species but also the range site that is most important by animal choice. Thus, the manager has something very concrete—a specific range site and the key plant—to aid him in management decisions. Obviously, these decisions are to determine the management require-

Fig. 69. In this mountain country the smooth, deep-soil sites with blue grama, the dominant grass, are grazed the most. Therefore, this is the key site and key grass to management, and when they are properly utilized no other part of the range will be over-utilized.

ments that will insure needed maintenance and improvement of the range for the highest sustained production possible.

Equipped with experience and the ability to interpret current usage of the range, the key range site and key species can be identified for any grazing unit. Once the range manager achieves this proficiency, he has to but examine those key areas for each pasture to determine his management potential or needed adjustments in management (Fig. 69).

WHEN IT IS IMPORTANT TO KNOW ABOUT UTILIZATION

Range forage utilization checks should be a routine procedure and should be continuous throughout the grazing period for any range. The adage "the eye of the master fattens the cattle" is equally important, or more so, with respect to maintenance of the grass. Grass management requires constant, close, and critical observation.

It is important to remain conversant not only with the extent of grazing but with what is being grazed at a particular time. Interpretation of these events provides an accumulative basis for timely decisions in management. With this knowledge and experience, these timely decisions might be termed critical periods of utilization. For summer growing plants, these periods are spring, during early stages of growth, and fall, the period when plant development and maturity are important. For plants that grow during the cool seasons, critical periods of utilization are somewhat different to conform to growth and development stages. Critical periods for most cool season plants are at the beginning of their growth in the fall and again as they approach maturity in late spring or early summer.

As a general rule, in the early stages of spring growth, animals of any and all kinds are not too discriminate in what they graze. After having been on dry feed during winter months, they have a craving for something green. Most any new growth that can be grazed will be taken, generally without regard to palatability. This may include plants that are poisonous or otherwise injurious to livestock.

On the other hand, indiscriminate early spring grazing can be used to an advantage in grazing management. In the first place, ravenous grazing of unwanted plants on the range may be very beneficial to the range, provided, of course, that they are not injurious to livestock. Using those plants then, at their highest state of nutrition, turns what might otherwise be wasted feed into livestock production. Furthermore, grazing those unwanted plants removes them from competition with better plants that are being managed for maintenance and improvement. Then too, early spring use may be a way to get production from what might be considered a desirable plant but which is palatable only in the early stages of growth. An example of such a plant might be several species of threeawn common on southwestern ranges often in competition with more desirable grasses. These species start spring growth as much as three weeks ahead of other perennial grasses, at which time they are palatable and nutritious. If abundant in the stand, they may carry the grazing load for thirty days, allowing better grasses to reach a stage of range readiness before being grazed to any extent.

With these advantages and disadvantages of early spring grazing, too much stress cannot be placed on the necessity of continuous observation of what is happening to the key grass on that range. Under no circumstance should the key grass be abusively grazed during its early spring growth stage. It is at that period of growth that it and all other good grasses are making their strongest bid for recovery growth. Old roots that have died off are being replaced. Vegetative stems are being produced that not only add sustenance to the plant itself but add to total forage production. Reproductive developments are taking place for perpetuation of the plant. And the general health and vigor of the plant are largely determined with spring growth and development.

The key to good range utilization in the spring and early summer, when the key plants begin to be selected and closely grazed, is judging when the grazing load should be adjusted. This is true, regardless of what the situation might be as to use or non-use of other species in the composition. The utilization of key plants at that critical stage of growth determines the trend range condition will take. If overuse is continued, the range will move toward a lower condition. If the key plants are not overused at that critical period, the range condition will be maintained and perhaps improved.

Owing to the importance of ranges not being utilized too heavily or too early in the spring, this has become an important criterion for the practice of range deferment. In fact, the definition for deferred grazing specifies complete non-use from the beginning of spring growth through the entire growing season. As a fundamental principle, no grazing system comprising a period of non-use should ever be intended to supplant the proven benefits of range rest during the entire growing season.

A second critical utilization period for ranges comprised primarily of warm season plants is the fall season. This is the time when physiological activities important to production, maintenance, and stability of plants are taking place. It is the stage of plant development during which plant food manufacture, translocation to the crown storage area, formation of next year's growth buds, and adjustments to plant maturity take place. During this stage of plant development, much growth energy goes to the development and maturity of seed or other reproduction processes.

Obviously, if these developments are to be satisfactory, plant requirements for growth and development must be met. They consist merely of the basic elements of plant growth: a home, consisting of a good soil and plenty of room for both a good root system and aerial development; freedom from excess competition for plant food, moisture, and sunlight; an adequate amount of green leaves and stems during and at the end of the growth period; and normal requirements of air and moisture to properly sustain the plant through dormancy. If these conditions are to prevail to a satisfactory degree, knowing that utilization has not been excessive at that time is most important to good management.

SEASONAL CHARACTERISTICS OF RANGE UTILIZATION

A degree of grazing at any season of the year may not be readily detected unless rather definite characteristics can be interpreted into range responses. The range manager needs to know these characteristics and be able to interpret them.

As a general rule, utilization checks are more difficult to make in the spring and early summer, owing to the usual luxuriant growth of a wider variety of plants than is common later in the season. Also, there is less selective grazing at that time, and, therefore, actually less likelihood of heavy use of key species.

Because of a usually lush growth of all plants in the spring, it is easy to overestimate the total volume of production. Or, perhaps of greater importance, it is difficult to recognize when the extra production is no longer contributing to the grazing load. These fallacies in judgment may be due to the fact that most of the grazing, up to that point, came from secondary plants; or perhaps those plants have become unpalatable and less nutritious, therefore grazing of them has ceased. For either or both reasons, grazing immediately becomes selective on the key species, resulting in too heavy use of the important grasses for management. It is at this point that adjustments in management need to be made.

Logical management means stocking the range in early spring to the capacity of the total forage production, including all grazable plants. When the grazing load gets ahead of the lush forage growth, the use being made of the important grasses immediately becomes a significant factor to management. Selective use of key plants will take place, and they will quickly reflect an overused condition. That is, stem and leaf growth will be consumed much faster than new growth will occur. When this pattern of grazing is noted, immediate steps should be taken to reduce the grazing load. A first choice would be a complete deferment until those better grasses recover to a state of grazing readiness. Thereafter, either light grazing or a deferred system of grazing is very desirable through the remainder of the production season and even through the dormant period.

Of equal or perhaps greater importance in judging utilization as the key to range management is noting characteristics of what has taken place in the fall near the end of the forage production period. At this time it is possible to make a more careful and accurate determination as to the amount of forage produced, the amount used, and the amount left. A careful analysis at this time is necessary, inasmuch as the growing season is about over, with little chance for additional production. In contrast, at any time earlier in the season there is a possibility for at least some additional regrowth to compensate for what might be a temporarily overgrazed condition.

It is in the fall season that planned management for proper use of that range must be determined. The management planned should result in the range not being overused at the end of the grazing season. On yearlong ranges, the end of the grazing season is considered to coincide with the beginning of spring growth.

When fall utilization checks and needed management adjustments are made, the range at the end of the grazing season should have definite use characteristics. Briefly, these may be identified as: good amounts of forage left, estimated at approximately 50 per cent of the current production; an estimated 25 per cent of seed stems remaining; and some plants of the key species in the composition not grazed at all. These characteristics apply primarily to the key range site when well removed from livestock concentrations, such as around water or salt locations.

RANCHER EVALUATION OF RANGE USE

In the overall management of ranch operations the rancher is confronted with many decisions. Time will not permit his detailed examination of each and every situation as a basis for making range management decisions. He must acquire a skill that will enable him to make reasonably accurate decisions commensurate with all phases of the operation. This can be done only through a planned approach and with an understanding of the objectives he wants to achieve.

Experience bears out the fact that range use evaluations to determine needed adjustments can be made more reliably at the end of a growing season. At that time the range is more static, free of undependable annuals, and there is no possibility of additional production to alter the evaluation.

In the preceding section, the general appearance of a properly used range at the end of the grazing season was described. The amount of forage remaining, the presence of seed stalks, and some ungrazed plants of the key species for management are the primary factors of evaluation.

These same factors are basic to range evaluations and planned management at any season of the year. They are of special significance to the rancher as he makes fall plans and adjustments for the remaining months of range use before a new forage crop starts. He must, of course, project the appearance of his range the following spring and thereby be knowledgeable as to the amount of forage available for use.

With this objective to planned management of rangeland, experience can be gained rather rapidly that will be well within the realm of reliable accuracy. In fact, these procedures are becoming commonplace among successful ranchers throughout the country.

As has been pointed out, the key to making reliable observational judgments is the use of a single species of grass, logically the best grass on the range. Having but one kind of grass and only the current year's production to be concerned with greatly simplifies observational evaluations. Then, when such an evaluation can be interpreted into the proper degree of grazing of the range and use planned to achieve that degree, the best treatment possible for that range will result. As a rule of thumb, the proper use factor is approximately half the production of the current or last season of growth.

A word of caution is always necessary when the terms "fifty per cent use of total production" or "take half and leave half the grass" are mentioned. In the first place, 50 per cent of total production does not mean half the height of a plant. Secondly, a greater portion (50 to 85 per cent) of a grass plant, by volume or by weight, is in the base of the plant. The top half of height growth of stems and leaves makes up a comparatively small portion of the total production.

On this premise it becomes necessary to know what 50 per cent of the plant in question, in its current state of production, actually looks like. An accepted procedure—perhaps rather unscientific but practical—is finding the mid-height point of an ungrazed plant. An average plant should be selected. Clip at crown level with a pocket knife, to include all of the current year's production but none of the previous year's growth. Tie a string around the clipped plant to make a tightly compressed sheaf. Balance the sheaf across a finger or the

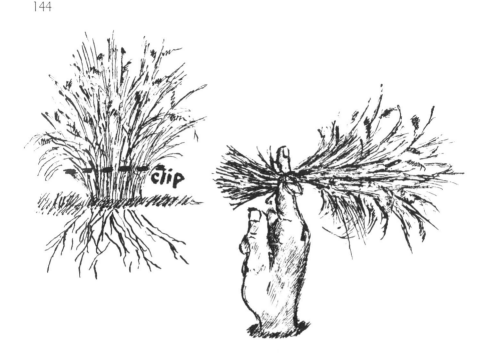

Fig. 70. A practical way to determine approximately half of the current production of a grass plant. (Drawing by Jack Douglas.)

blade of a knife. At the focal point the sheaf will remain in a horizontal position. That portion at the basal end of the plant represents the 50 per cent that should remain unused, and the portion above that represents the 50 per cent available for use without overuse of the plant (Fig. 70).

By this simple procedure a reliable judgment can be made as to a proper degree of use for that range and for that particular year. Such a judgment should, however, be tempered by the knowledge that animals do not graze plants evenly as if clipped with a knife, clipper, or mower. Some plants will be grazed with shorter and some with longer stubble than the balance method might have shown. Also, seed stems must not be overlooked. With a properly used range they will be there in about the right proportion. If there are none, the range is obviously overused, and measurements are unnecessary.

By using this simple procedure the rancher can, at any time during the grazing period, make a fair estimate of the amount of forage left to be grazed before overuse would occur.

UTILIZATION CHECKS BY SAMPLING AND MEASURING

There are times when more accurate utilization determinations are important. A procedure in use by the Soil Conservation Service, and possibly other technical groups, is accurate for field determination, easily applied, and practical. Briefly the procedure is as follows:

Select the key range site and key species of that site for the pasture or range being evaluated. Select an area of that site that has had average use for the current grazing period; that is, one that has neither had an undue amount of use owing to concentration of live-stock nor that might have been used less than average for any reason. Predetermine a line of traverse across the area to be evaluated. A minimum of fifty sample plants should be measured. Thus, a pre-determined sample frequency and spacing of samples can be made. To make the evaluation, make the traverse by counting paces and stopping on the pace predetermined for sampling. The plant of the key species nearest the toe of the designated pace is the one to be measured.

Use two containers (paper sacks are most practical) in the pro-cedure. One is for plants that have been grazed to any degree as determined by close examination if necessary. The other is for plants of the species that have not been grazed. Clip the sample plant (cur-rent year's production only) at crown level and place it in the appro-priate sack for grazed or ungrazed plants. Keep a record of the num-ber of plants placed in each sack. When the traverse is completed (fifty plants or more), carefully weigh both samples and record the weights. By using the total weight of the ungrazed plants, determine the average weight per plant. Multiply the average weight per plant by the total number of plants sampled (total ungrazed plus total grazed plants). This total weight of both grazed and ungrazed plants is the weight of forage still remaining. Subtract the weight of forage remaining from the total production weight to arrive at the weight of forage already used. Divide the weight of used forage by the weight of total forage produced to obtain the percentage used.

Example:

wt of 5 ungrazed plants = 30 gms
wt of 45 grazed plants = 180 gms
30 gms ÷ 5 plants = 6 gms av wt of ungrazed plants
6 gms × 50 plants (in sample) = 300 gms total wt of sample of not
     grazed
180 gms + 30 gms = 210 gms—wt of ungrazed plus wt of grazed
     samples left
300 gms — 210 gms = 80 gms already used
80 gms ÷ 300 gms = 26.6% used

More precise methods of determining range utilization have been developed for use in research and statistical analysis work. However, the above described field procedure has proved reliable and satisfactory for range management determinations. It can be used by the rancher or the technician to sharpen his estimates.

JUDGING RANGE UTILIZATION OF POOR CONDITION RANGES

The question of what constitutes proper use of ranges in poor condition is one of paramount importance, yet it is difficult to pinpoint. Very often what would normally be a reliable key species for the site is only minor or possibly completely gone out of the composition. If it is in minor quantity, certainly its maintenance and increase in abundance over the range should be of primary concern in the management plan. On the other hand, if proper use of that range is based on the utilization of such a small portion of the total forage, very little use would be made of that range. In many instances, practically no use beyond the practical limits of most ranching operations could be made of it.

Under such circumstances of poor range condition, a logical approach is to select the best species available. It must be in sufficient amount to carry a reasonable portion of the grazing load to be a suitable grass on which to base management. That would normally be the species grazed most among those present. To be reliable, only perennial plants should be considered, and they should remain palatable throughout most of the grazing season or year on yearlong ranges.

When conditions make it necessary to use secondary plants to judge range utilization, two basic principles of management must be taken into account: (1) Adjust the grazing use to get as much as possible from the low-grade plants when they are palatable and nutritious, and at the same time reduce them from competition with the lesser amounts of more desirable species. (2) Adjust the grazing use to provide full benefit for growth and development of the better grasses, even though they may be only minor in the stand.

A logical rest period for most range grasses under these conditions is the last 30 to 45 days of the growing season. This is adequate only if growing conditions are favorable at the time. This period is particularly critical because it is the time when vegetative growth is necessary for the manufacture of plant food. Also at this time, translocation and storage of reserve food supplies and bud formation for next year's growth take place. Of near equal importance is consideration of those plants during the spring and early summer growth period. That is the time when plants grow most vigorously and expand in crown coverage, in root system, and in new plant establishment, either from stolons, rhizomes, or seedlings. However, these developments take place only when the necessary growth requirements have been provided at the end of the previous growing season.

Protective management at both these critical periods is desirable. But if this is not possible, the range manager will have a decision to make after consideration of all factors involved. When only a single period can be given preference treatment within the year, switching treatment between the two seasons in alternate years is a practical approach to the problem. Where this type of management is necessary, a more intensive program of manipulating the livestock is necessary than where range conditions are higher and more stable (Fig. 71).

When only one or two pastures of a ranching operation require more restrictive utilization standards for improvement, the management plan can usually encompass necessary use requirements without too much difficulty. But when all pastures of the operation require preferred treatment, the plan will of necessity be more complex. When these conditions occur, it is usually practical to select one or two pastures on which intensive management will be applied. As they improve, other pastures can be included until the entire ranch is on the upward trend with definite indicators of improved range condition. It is usually beneficial to start an improvement program on the best pasture rather than on the poorest pasture. The

Fig. 71. On a severely depleted range, there often is no reliable plant to use in judging utilization. The most severe management, such as complete deferment, will be required to restore this range to productive use.

better pasture will respond more quickly, thereby contributing more to the ranching operation. Furthermore, the poor pasture will not be greatly damaged beyond the condition it is already in, until such time as it can be included in the improvement plan.

UTILIZATION WHERE BOTH WARM SEASON AND COOL SEASON GRASSES OCCUR

In some climates there are ranges that support an abundance of both warm season and cool season plants. Often, both groups of plants contribute materially to a desirable forage production for the ranch. Examples of this condition are found in the southern Plains and southern part of the subhumid zone of rangeland, especially in Oklahoma and Texas. In these areas of normally warm season forage production, species of needlegrass and western wheatgrass are often found in broad areas of valleys and bottomlands.

Where such conditions exist, there are two practical utilization evaluations available to the rancher. He may elect to manage the grazing unit as a cool season forage producing unit, or he may use it as a warm season forage producing unit. Whichever choice he makes, he would base his management of proper use on the appropriate type of plants, cool season or warm season. This would usually mean a bonus to the extent of production of the other type of forage. That bonus could be used as it would best fit into his management plan without seriously interfering with production and management of the primary forage crop at critical periods. Obviously, this would result in a more complex system of management than if only a single type of forage was involved.

An alternative type of management would be to recognize the two types of vegetation and develop management around two distinct seasons of use within the year. Such a management plan can be operated most easily if fencing arrangements separate the two types of vegetation into grazing units. But, on the other hand, such a plan is operative without fenced units. This, however, could be based only on seasonal choice of grazing by the livestock and by grazing intensities being adjusted accordingly.

The latter plan of management would require more careful observations and evaluations of the grazing pattern. It would also require a more complex management plan for the ranch as a whole.

Of particular significance, where cool and warm season vegetation is in the same pasture, and where no definite plan of management is carried out, is the stocking rate. Too often, without a plan, such pastures are stocked yearlong at so many acres per animal unit. This would not be too bad if the per cent of each type of vegetation in the pasture and the percentage of time of seasonal palatability for each type within the year coincided. Seldom is this the case, and as a result there are invariably too many livestock for too long a period of time on one or the other type of vegetation. Thus, range deterioration on that portion of the range is inevitable.

Chapter 9

PROPER GRAZING USE OF
FORAGE PRODUCTION

Proper grazing use of the range, the most significant principle of range management. Proper use paramount to the highest production from the range. A practical definition and statement of objectives as guidance to good range and livestock management. Evaluation of grazing use on the key site and species, the criterion to current production and management. How ranges deteriorate with over use and improve with proper use. Overall benefits from proper grazing use of range forage. How ranges respond to management that will insure proper grazing use of the forage.

This chapter and the next three deal with the four cardinal principles of range management: (1) range proper use; (2) proper season of use; (3) proper distribution of grazing; and (4) proper kind of livestock. This chapter also deals with proper use of the forage and the way the range responds to that use.

The phrase "range proper use" has become commonplace both in writing and in conversation on the subject of range management. With professional people, and with many ranchers, it has come to be a stock in trade statement, but with all too liberal an interpretation.

The range proper use concept is perhaps the most significant concern if good range management and livestock production are the objectives. To be meaningful as a guide to good range management and a symbol to sound ranching operations, it must be thoroughly understood and readily interpreted on the range. That is, it must be recognizable in all its various complexities of environment and use. And it must be measured in terms that can be seen and understood.

The degree of range use is plainly imprinted on the landscape. Too often it is merely recognized as "plenty of grass," or "that grass is getting short," or possibly, "out of grass." The rancher is logically concerned with his entire ranching operation from the standpoint of how much grass he has or how much has been used. He is also concerned about each grazing unit or pasture which is his primary management unit for both his range and his livestock. But the one who makes a true evaluation of the use that is made of the range must be more specific than the use of a single pasture or the entire range. There must be a more precise unit of measure if the grazing use is to be evaluated as the index to range management. The individual range site and individual plants selected for grazing furnish the true criteria to range proper use. More specifically, they are provided by the key grazing site for each pasture or range and the key species on that site that must be evaluated.

To review the role of the key plant in determining the degree of range use, it can be considered the "best" plant or species on that range as far as the livestock are concerned. This does not necessarily mean it is the best that will grow on a key grazing site. But it is the best on the favored site at a particular time, under existing range conditions, which may vary from excellent to poor. In addition to being a first-choice species by the livestock, it also has other characteristics that are important. It very likely will be the species that carries most of the grazing load. It will be palatable and nutritious over a longer period of the grazing season or year than other plants that are growing with it. It will be a comparatively high yielder and quick to respond to good growth conditions. It will be palatable and nutritious with maturity and will be stable in the composition. And, unless the range is seriously depleted, it will be climax to the site as either a decreaser or a strong increaser.

DEFINITION AND OBJECTIVES OF RANGE PROPER USE

Range proper use may be practically defined as grazing a range to a degree that will permit the best forage plants to make full use of the environment for maximum development during the current production season. This means that the choice species, as determined by persistent use by grazing animals, is not grazed beyond its ability to maintain itself in competition with all others that are growing there.

This is done only when enough of those plants are left ungrazed to insure the necessary functioning of leaves and stems in the manufacture of sufficient plant food to sustain a healthy and vigorous condition (Fig. 72). When grazed beyond this point, a plant cannot

Fig. 72. Little bluestem is the key grass in judging the degree of grazing use on this good condition range. These plants have not been excessively used by near the end of the grazing season.

Fig. 73. Blue grama is the key grass on this low, fair condition range. It has been closely grazed and the range over used, but an abundance of sand dropseed gives the appearance of plenty of grass.

function normally; therefore, it becomes weakened and cannot fully develop. In contrast, other plants growing in the composition that are not selected at all, or only to a lesser degree by the grazing animals, do have full benefit of their food processing devices and therefore remain strong and vigorous (Fig. 73). They have every advantage over the plant that was weakened by being grazed beyond its growth requirements. This is the first step toward plant retrogression or range deterioration. However, this is seldom noticed until the stage has been reached where definite plant changes in the composition have taken place.

At the outset, these preliminary changes may not seriously affect range production, but may quickly influence grazing habits of the livestock. The loss of their first-choice grazing plants may cause them to seek other sites and species as first choice, which serves as a good indicator that something has changed on that range. Generally, differences in grazing will include heavier use farther away from water, more intensive use of less desirable sites, or heavier use of less desirable plants. In addition, production of the range has declined as these changes take place. These early changes are indicators of needed adjustments in management of the range.

EVALUATING USE MADE OF KEY GRAZING SITES

As previously discussed, the key grazing site will be the area of a grazing unit that is used most consistently and over a longer period of time than any other site available to the livestock. The rancher will know with no uncertainty where, at what season, and the extent to which his livestock use various range sites, especially the ones they like best and use most.

Also, if he knows the more important plants, the rancher will readily observe which ones are being taken and when. And, based on judgment and perhaps a little training, he can know the approximate degree of use that has been made of the key species, or any other species that may seem significant to use and management of the range.

When grazed to the proper degree without penalizing the best plants, the key range site very likely will have the appearance of what might be considered wasted feed. This is far from being true when all factors, including pounds of forage and pounds of beef, are taken into account. At the end of the grazing season, when properly used, the key site may be described as: having some plants of the key species not grazed at all; the overall use that has been made of the key species will be 50 per cent or less, by weight of total production for the species; less desirable forage plants will be grazed little or none; unpalatable plants will not have been grazed other than a possible nip here and there, probably to test palatability; browse plants, if present in a grass range and if palatable, will be lightly grazed, and perhaps only for variety in the diet; and the site will be uniformly grazed except possibly around areas of concentration, such as water and salt locations.

Obviously, a site with this general appearance at the end of the grazing season will be ragged and look as though much good forage has gone to waste. This will be particularly true when the site is in a lower range condition as fair or poor. At the outset of a range improvement program, and especially when in the lower range conditions, there will be some unused forage, that is, forage that was used when grazing pressure and overuse had been the practice.

This non-use of secondary plants may be considered a penalty, but it is not. That non-use will be more than compensated for as the range improves as a result of being properly grazed. How quickly such compensation will come about is not a specifically answerable question. Factors that will influence improvement are: how far down the condition scale the range has retrogressed; how strongly the downward trend was progressing before the improvement program was initiated; the amount and vigor of the key plants present in the composition; the amount and character of plants that have invaded the site, as perennial weeds and brush; the ever present weather factor; and the productive capacity of the soil.

This does not mean that some profitable use cannot be made of those less desirable range plants when ranges are being properly grazed in an improvement program. In the first place, some use will be made of them, since all livestock will select a variety of plants in their diet. Then, too, the grazing system may well include short periods of concentrated grazing to make use of certain plants with brief periods of palatability. And carryover forage, even though of comparatively low quality, will often serve as filler after the primary grazing period or year is about over. For example, rather heavy use of a properly used pasture, just prior to the beginning of new growth, would not result in damage to the pasture. This is particularly true if done when supplemental protein feed is being given the livestock.

Although never planned and scheduled, carryover feed of any quality can be used in times of inadequate rainfall. This is not to say that such practice would not be detrimental to the range, but it would be less detrimental than to continue use of an already severely overused range when the drought comes.

CURRENT PRODUCTION AND PROPER GRAZING USE

There are several methods and techniques for measuring range vegetation and the degree of range use. The intensity of the procedure used depends on the precise use to be made of the information. To be useful to the rancher, a procedure must provide criteria that can be readily detected and interpreted. It must be something on which a sound judgment and management decisions can be made. Such a procedure was described in detail in Chapter 8.

The first prerequisite for the rancher to judge production and the degree of grazing is to know the key site and the key species of that site in each grazing unit or pasture. This need not be a repeat determination, since livestock will have indicated their grazing preference on a particular site not only during the current grazing period but through the years. This will be reliable experience information gained by the observing rancher.

If he is correct in his judgment as to the key range site and key forage species, that will be the only area and those will be the only plants he needs to be concerned about. If that area is not overused at the end of the grazing year, he can be assured that the entire grazing unit will not be overused. That is, if the key site and key species are properly used, the remainder of the pasture will take care of itself. With experience, gained by close observation, it will become second nature with the rancher to observe little telltale indicators of proper grazing use as well as improper or over grazing use of a pasture. He becomes competent in reading the landscape. Those key plants will become as real and significant to him as are his animals that use the range (Fig. 74). Noticeable use of less-desirable plants will become a warning to him. Grazing farther out from water and salt, and more constant use of sites other than the key site, will be an indication to him. A significant exception to this latter use indicator, however, is the seasonal selection of plants from other sites that is only a recognized part of proper use of the range.

Fig. 74. To an observant rancher, the condition of his range and current use that has been made of it are as important as the condition of his livestock. (Photo courtesy U.S. Soil Conservation Service, Texas.)

RANGE DETERIORATION WITH OVER-USE

When a range is used beyond its proper degree, the earmarks of a deteriorating range appear very rapidly. The first evidence of over-use will be the key forage species on the key site grazed beyond approximately 50 per cent of their current production. A first indication of a heavier than proper degree of use will be the absence of seed stalks. Or, if such use is prior to the seeding stage, destructive use of seed stem formation will be in evidence.

Another early evidence of over-use will be noticeable use of plants other than the key species. If this situation is not corrected at this stage, all grazable plants on the range will be taken, much in order

Fig. 75. A blue grama range over used for several years. Note how buffalograss, an increaser, has taken over. Sand dropseed, threeawn, and mesquite have invaded the range.

of their palatability. With continued overuse, even the most un-palatable, difficult to graze, and ultimately injurious plants will be taken indiscriminately in the grazing pattern.

With this degree of grazing, the key grass becomes just another grass, taken according to its availability. But without exception, it and all the better species in the composition will be grazed far beyond their ability to contribute to their own growth requirements. This, of course, is the primary reason for the decline of the health and vigor of all plants that are used beyond the proper degree. They not only decline in vigor but decrease in size and ability to compete with one another. Ultimately the weaker plants—and generally it will be the better, more severely grazed plants that become weakened first—will go out. This leaves space for the less-desirable increasing plants to take over until they too succumb to the ravages of heavy grazing and are eliminated. This is followed by the next successive step, which is the taking over by, or invasion of, outlaw plants that are standing by awaiting the opportunity to invade the area.

By the end of the grazing season or year, the overused range will have an "out of grass" appearance. If a high condition range is grazed

Fig. 76. A blue grama range seldom if ever over used, even in years of low production. This is a near undisturbed stand with but few increaser or invading plants in evidence.

heavily and well beyond the proper degree of use, even for a single year, the "out of grass" appearance likely will be the only readily noticeable evidence of overuse. However, with continued use beyond that which is proper, within a year or so, other indicators of range deterioration will be evident (Fig. 75). These include a greater predominance of increaser plants, a weakened and deteriorated condition of the key plants, invading plants very prominent in the composition, bare ground and erosion, and a lower-producing range, as would be indicated by livestock production.

PROPER RANGE USE AND RANGE IMPROVEMENT

In contrast to the deteriorated appearance of an overused or improperly used range, one that has been properly used will have many indicators to substantiate that fact. Rather than having an "out of grass" appearance, it may have an underused appearance (Fig. 76). Such an appearance, however, should not be misleading, as unused grass is not wasted grass. It is important as a first step in the process of range improvement. By any unit of measure, the high-condition, properly used range will furnish more pounds of usable forage than the total production in pounds of forage from the low-condition, overused range. Furthermore, the properly used high-condition range will have the ability to maintain itself indefinitely.

Under these conditions of use, plants will remain vigorous and in the highest state of production. And they will withstand most any weather cycle of good years and bad that are sure to come. This is not to say, however, that even the strongest of range plants cannot be adversely affected by prolonged drought periods. But it is true that strong plants will withstand severe droughts and respond to favorable conditions much more rapidly and completely than will weakened plants. Such response of a range is usually in direct relation to the abundance of the better plants in the composition, with the key species being the main criterion of survival and improvement.

Even with a low-range condition, with proper use there will be distinct indicators of that use. Among the more prominent ones is the general appearance of an unused or very lightly used range. Little or no use will have been made of unpalatable plants and plants that are coarse or otherwise difficult to graze. Most grazing will be on open, more accessible parts of the range. There will be some un-grazed plants of the key species. A cover, even though of the lower quality plants, will become noticeable near water and salt locations. There will be less trailing to and from water and salt. And browse plants, if present, will be grazed very little with no sign of hedging, as would be the appearance with overuse. These indicators will be known and used as criteria to grazing use by the observant rancher. Needless to say, at the outset, proper use of a low-condition range cannot possibly be as productive as it will become with improvement. Nor will it be as productive as when the low-condition plants were being heavily grazed. At that time, everything was being taken and nothing was returned for plant and soil maintenance.

OTHER BENEFITS FROM RANGE PROPER USE

Although the primary objective in properly grazing a range is to favor the various forage plants and achieve the potential of the range, there are other very distinct benefits to be had. Of significant importance is the stability lent to the range, which consists of soil and plants. With an improved plant cover resulting from properly grazing the range, the best and most practical protection to the land has been provided. A plant cover, which includes both the above-ground and below-ground parts of the plant, serves as a cushion to the impact of beating rain. Water reaches the soil more gently, thereby reducing compaction, nearly eliminating soil splash, which is the beginning of soil erosion, and water penetration is greatly improved. Soil stability on rangeland is that simple.

A covered soil is also protected from what might otherwise be damaging temperature effects. Bare soil will absorb the sun's rays, reaching temperatures of 125 to 140 degrees Fahrenheit in the southwest. Such temperatures are not only destructive to plant life, especially when weakened and unprotected, but will also destroy or drive to lower soil depths the biological life that is necessary to a productive soil. In addition, an uncovered soil is exposed to extremely cold temperatures that also adversely affect plant and biological life.

An adequate plant cover contributes to optimum benefits from soil particles, soil water, soil air, and soil temperature. These optimum benefits result in a condition identified as water stable aggregates. This may be described in simple terms as a flaky structure of soil particles and organic material fused together, in contrast to individual soil particles that form a compacted, impenetrable soil mass. With this latter condition, penetration of water, air, and even plant roots is severely restricted. This is an important facet of range deterioration. A stable, well-managed soil is a first requirement to a stable plant cover that can be properly managed.

Another significant advantage of a range properly grazed is the uniform use of all the range. In contrast, under the pressure of over grazing, livestock are in competition with one another. Each animal works hard to get its share of a limited amount of forage. This means that, by instinct, that animal will pressure graze where the quantity of forage is limited. This is especially true where there is only a limited amount of high-quality feed. Under such conditions, the animal may very well graze over a comparatively small area, completely covering it two or three times within a grazing period. This pattern of grazing will continue day after day, especially on the better sites in a pasture.

In contrast to this pattern of pressure grazing, when the range is properly grazed there is more freedom from competitive grazing among animals. They can graze leisurely, soon get their fill, rest, or go to water at their will. Because of this freedom from pressure grazing, contentment and self satisfaction seem to prevail. In turn, most domestic livestock seem to have more time to explore the range, travel over less-attractive sites, and even range farther away from water. In this process they naturally encounter fresh, unused plants of the better kinds. And, of equal importance, they find a variety of forage that is attractive and beneficial to them. Thus, by the mere process of properly grazing the range, all range sites and all forage plants, both good and bad, will be used and converted into livestock products.

A third, and most important, advantage of properly grazing the range lies in the fact that there will always be a carryover of reserve feed for emergency use. Much of the western range country is in comparatively low-rainfall zones. Periodic droughts are common, as is a shortage of range forage. Under any set of conditions, proper use of the range will insure a carryover that can be used in an emergency. This would amount to the unused half of the key plants, as well as the remaining half or more of secondary plants. Although this forage is recognized as a source of emergency feed, emergency use is not advisable as a general practice. Too often, emergency operations become normal and lead to the downfall of any semblance of proper range use.

Even though this reserve forage from proper use should be maintained for its benefit to the land and to the forage crop, occasional emergency use of it is not too bad. The range that is managed on the basis of proper use of the forage is strong, productive, and stable. Adapted plants have the stamina to withstand drought periods. Furthermore, they can withstand grazing, possibly heavy grazing, during such periods. During the growing season with a deficiency of rainfall, some grazing of the range to use current growth and some of the carryover is beneficial. The removal of moisture using plant development actually removes the plant from competition with itself. The mother plant will be maintained more completely from the crown down, without having to support both the above-ground and below-ground parts of the plant. A word of caution is in order. This principle of drought use is far more logical and beneficial to a range in high condition than one in low condition. If the range condition is low, there will be an abundance of poor quality plants, and lesser amounts of good plants. In grazing that type of range, the good plants will be grazed, leaving the poor quality plants to compete strongly for the limited moisture that may be available. This would be a disadvantage for the plants that should be improved, and an advantage for the less-desirable plants.

Competition among range plants is a fourth advantage of proper range use. It is a fact that in the plant kingdom those species best adapted to an environment will persist if given a chance. It is also known that when these adapted or climax plants are disturbed to the extent that their growth requirements are impaired, they become weakened and deteriorated. Eventually, with continued abuse, they will give way completely. By the process of plant retrogression, other less-desirable plants will move in, taking the place of the deteriorated better plants. But once the treatment of abusive grazing use is reversed, the better plants will again be provided their growth requirements and can and will re-establish themselves. This is the objective, and these are the processes that take place with good range management.

Range management, good or bad, is predicated on competition among range plants. Once the climax is established, it will hold its own, with minor fluctuation of losses and re-establishment of plants, provided competition from secondary plants is not permitted to dominate. In the forest, the first disturbance is cutting of climax trees. On the range, it is heavy use of climax forage plants. In both instances the process is detrimental to the stand of climax plants. Those climax plants, trees or grass, are robbed of their ability to take full advantage of their environment. If allowed to continue, this deterioration makes more room and more natural growth requirements available to plants that have not been grazed or harvested beyond their growth requirements.

As these conditions prevail, the productivity of the range becomes less and less. This has been the fate of much of the once productive and profitable rangelands throughout the world. But, fortunately, there remains much of the range country that can be restored to its near-original productivity just by the simple process of range proper use. This is essential to the maintenance of any range. And no treatment, regardless of how intensive, spectacular, or costly, will take the place of range proper use if the grazing resource is to be established and maintained.

Fig. 77. A heavy infestation of brush precludes improvement from proper grazing use of this range. Competition for water, plant food, and the shading effect prevents much, if any, response from management. (Photo courtesy U.S. Soil Conservation Service, Texas.)

RANGE RESPONSE TO PROPER USE

How quickly a range will respond to proper grazing use depends on how far down it is in range condition. Also, the low-condition factors, such as the presence or absence of competitive plants, weakened climax plants, or the amount of the key plants left on the range, affect the response to proper use.

Much of the western range country has declined in production without having lost all of the principal climax plants. This reduced

Fig. 78. Weeds are as detrimental to grass production as is the brush on this range. Although a dense stand, they afford little protection and stability to the soil. (Photo courtesy U.S. Soil Conservation Service, Texas.)

production has come about from rather consistent overuse of the range. Individual plants have become weakened and low-producing through starvation. That is, by continually keeping green growth, leaves, and stems grazed below the 50 per cent necessary for plant maintenance, the livestock continue to stay ahead of the grass. It never has a chance to catch up to the grazing pressure, therefore it can never get ahead or gain in its production.

Regardless of the kind of range plants involved, when this condition exists they cannot respond immediately to any kind of management treatment. When proper use is applied, that means taking no more than half of the current production. Even so, half of a low yield of the key plant will still leave but little of the food manufacturing parts of those plants. In fact, the gain in this respect may be negligible at the outset.

Under these conditions, it will take several years before gains in plant growth and production will be noted. But with persistence and close adherence to the principles of proper grazing use, headway will be made each year until the objective is achieved. It took many years of overuse and declining range condition to reach the all too common unproductive range condition. Likewise, it will take a comparable period of time to correct the condition.

A further note of discouragement from the practice of proper use deals with excessive amounts of overstory competitive plants (Fig. 77). Brush and tree growth that provides an overstory and shading effect, in addition to competition for food and water, will almost preclude much, if any, response from proper grazing use of the range. Under these conditions, little gain can be expected from any management of the range until this competition has been removed. An abundance of weeds and weedy grasses on the range may be almost as prohibitive to range response (Fig. 78), but much can be done with them through various range management and livestock manipulation practices.

Chapter 10

SEASON OF USE IN RANGE MANAGEMENT

Importance of season of use to proper range use. Livestock, the most reliable indicator of proper seasonal use of ranges. Seasonal use preferences of range sites, that are important to management of rangeland. Seasonal palatability and nutritional characteristics of kinds of plants, that affect management. Wide variation of the terrain of a country in regard to adaptations and seasonal preferences by kinds of livestock. Seasonal limitations imposed by temperature and insect pests on some kinds of rangelands. Importance to good range and livestock management of ranch improvements to facilitate seasonal use and adjustments.

Next in importance to the basic principle of range proper use is proper season of use. It is so closely allied to and supplemental to proper use, that separating one from the other, either in discussion or practice, is very difficult. In fact, proper season of use is merely a way of achieving maximum use of the range without violating the principle of range proper use. And, as will be noted in subsequent chapters, it is also a significant criterion in the application of the other two basic principles of range management, namely, distribution of grazing and kind of livestock suited to the range.

In a ranching operation, season of use is achieved only by manipulation of livestock. When not restricted by fences or other barriers, grazing animals will make their own seasonal adjustments. This is not always to the best interest of livestock production. Thus, fencing arrangements to control livestock and insure proper seasonal use of various parts of the range is important to good management. Seldom is it practical to fence into separate units every area of distinct seasonal qualities of grazing. Therefore, controlled manipulation of the livestock may become an intricate part of management.

To consider seasonal use in grazing management, it is important to know and understand why plants are selected for grazing when they are. There is always a reason for a consistent pattern of seasonal use to be established.

THE RANGE SITE INFLUENCES SEASON OF USE

Perhaps of first importance is the range site. The site is relevant not only to the kind of plants that are to be found but also to the nutritive quality of them. The soil of a range site, with its inherent fertility level, is the regulator of available moisture, especially through the productive season. This is due, of course, to the water holding capacity of the soil as determined by depth, texture, and organic content. The amount of water that falls or runs onto the site is also a determining factor. These two factors account for the generally high production and preference of use given a bottomland or valley site.

The soil-moisture relationship, along with other site characteristics, is responsible for the kind of plants that grow on the site (Figs. 79 and 80). Many different vegetation characteristics will result from the numerous site factors that do exist. Among them is the important characteristic of phenology or seasonal plant development and the corresponding quality. Very often, individual range sites produce plants with distinct seasonal qualities, making those sites unique in a grazing management plan. Sometimes these seasonal site characteristics may be mechanical as a result of structure of the plant, or they may be nutritional, but in either instance they are significant. A site adapted to the production of cool season grasses is distinct from one adapted to warm season grasses. On the other hand, a site with a near pure stand of blue grama may appear little different from another site with a mixture of half blue grama and half hairy grama. Yet, the latter site has a distinct use characteristic in that hairy grama generally is taken by preference in the fall months. This should be considered in the grazing management plan, if the best use and proper use is to be made of that site.

In consideration of range site characteristics that influence seasonal use, soil condition cannot be overlooked. With a downward trend in range condition, and especially as fair and poor condition is approached, the physical condition of the soil also deteriorates. To this extent, both water intake and the water holding capacity of the soil decrease. At the same time, the soil surface is exposed to the ele-

Fig. 79. In a 10–12 inch rainfall, on a deep sandy loam soil, mesquite and grama grasses are indicative of the kinds of plants that will grow.

Fig. 80. In contrast to the type of vegetation in Fig. 79, a shallow site in the same area will support nothing but desert type plants. Lecheguilla, various cacti, fluff grass, and red grama are on this site.

Fig. 81. A nearly pure stand of alkali sacaton, which is very seasonal as to palatability. Once this area had good amounts of sideoats grama, blue grama, and other grasses, along with the sacaton. (Photo courtesy U.S. Soil Conservation Service, Texas.)

ments of the environment, incurring intense temperatures, loss of organic matter, and surface crusting. This induces water runoff and erosion, which are early stages of reduced production from the range. Coincident with this deterioration will be a change in the kind of plants that dominate the site. These changes will usually be characterized by differences in the season of palatability and nutritive quality of the forage. As these changes occur, so do the grazing preferences of the livestock. Too often these changes are the beginning of declining production from both the range and the livestock.

Even under the best of management and range condition, there are site characteristics that result in distinct kinds of vegetation that is decidedly seasonal in production and use. These conditions may be of such significance as to affect an entire ranching operation. An example is sizable areas of near pure stands of tobosa grass on a ranch. This condition would impose a very definite seasonal pattern of use on that area, which would, in turn, affect management and use of the rest of the ranch. Another example is areas infested with a plant-like redberry juniper, which promotes a heat and insect problem requiring seasonal use adjustments affecting the entire ranch.

Fig. 82. Practically all grasses except tobosa have been grazed out on this range. It can be ranched yearlong, but at much less than the potential of the range. (Photo courtesy U.S. Soil Conservation Service, Texas.)

KINDS OF VEGETATION AND SEASON OF USE

Natural differences in site productivity are evidenced by distinctly different kinds of vegetation that are seasonal, particularly as to when they will be grazed. Failure to recognize this has resulted in the near ruination of vast areas of rangeland throughout the country. Unfortunately, these areas have too often been some of the more productive rangelands, such as valleys and bottomlands along stream courses.

In the southwest there are now extensive areas on which the dominant forage is near pure stands of such species as tobosa grass (*Hilaria mutica*), galleta (*Hilaria jamesi*), alkali sacaton (*Sporobolus airoides*), threeawn (*Aristida sp.*), and possibly other species, that have developed as a result of improper management (Fig. 81). Generally, these areas are very seasonal as to palatability and nutritional quality of forage. Some such areas are essentially beyond restoration by anything short of reclamation treatment. Consequently, there are today vast areas with these conditions being ranched on a yearlong basis but with much less than their potential production (Fig. 82).

Other extensive areas approach this stage of depletion, but in locales where there are remnants of better grasses that can be improved through management. Such areas will respond rather quickly, and to a substantial degree, from grazing management, with seasonal use and subsequent rest being paramount in the grazing plan. Such a plan would include a grazing period, and possibly rather heavy grazing, at the time of highest palatability of the undesirable, dominant species. This use period should be followed by a rest period beginning at the time the dominant species becomes unpalatable. When grazing of the less desirable species ceases and animals start searching for the better plants, the pasture should be vacated immediately. In any instance, the rest period must extend through most of the current growing season. This will insure an opportunity for those better plants to recuperate and develop from the heavy use they inevitably received earlier in the season.

From the livestock production standpoint, use during the season of highest palatability is important even though there are no desirable plants to improve. Here the range manager needs to be concerned only about the grazing quality of the dominant grass that is only seasonally palatable and nutritious. When desirable plants do not exist, the grazing period may well continue as long as there is usable forage, and livestock are not losing weight. Under these conditions, a heavier than normal rate of stocking is usually advisable.

Such practice may be termed concentrated grazing. It achieves two objectives, one of economic importance and the other of technical importance. By concentrating numbers on such areas when palatability is highest, more use and therefore more livestock production can be had before the grass becomes unpalatable. With a moderate, or what might be considered a proper rate of stocking, forage production will likely be in excess of total consumption during the palatable period. Thus, an accumulation of old grass will occur, which is objectionable from a range management standpoint. When this condition does prevail, there is a distinct advantage to be had from livestock trampling where there is an excess of plant growth. This is particularly true with excess growth of seasonally palatable grasses such as tobosa, galleta, and threeawn. Disturbance from trampling, plus as much grazing use as possible, eliminates at least some of the competition by this excessive growth of seasonally palatable grass. Opening up an otherwise dense cover or accumulation of old growth stimulates both the soil and any desirable plant that might chance to enter the area. It makes possible more effective use of sunlight and air, two essential ingredients of the complexity of requirements for an improving range.

Throughout the range country there are many plants that are distinctly seasonal, either as to when they grow or when they are palatable, or possibly both. Generally, where there are many and varied species of plants that are seasonal, both the problem and the solution are much less distinct than where a single species dominates the area, as described above. For the most part, these seasonal plants are strong increasers of the climax vegetation, or they are plants that have invaded the site.

Because of their admixture in a plant community where important forage plants occur, their use and management become more complicated in a management plan. Very often it is necessary to do more than usual or desirable manipulation of livestock to get the most from that range without damage to it. It is safe to say, however, that seasonal use closely allied with proper use becomes the focal point to management.

The use of spring and early summer annuals that heavily infest some ranges can best be accomplished by a seasonal use period when they are lush and nutritious. In like manner, cool season annual and perennial grasses, particularly on southern and southwestern ranges, require a period of seasonal use in the spring if the most is to be gotten from them. They often contribute materially to efficient livestock production.

Another aspect of the principle of seasonal use as related to kinds of plants is concerned with those plants that might be noxious or otherwise injurious to livestock. Where these conditions exist, the practice of seasonal use may actually include a season of non-use. However, a period of non-use may often be preceded by a period of productive concentrated use. Such would be the case where an early spring growth of one of the stipas or threeawn would be followed by a massive production of awns to contaminate wool and mohair. Here, heavy early use would have contributed to livestock production that will help offset non-use during the period of mechanical injury to sheep and goats.

Another example of seasonal non-use of a range is where shinnery oak is present. It is strongly poisonous during the bud stage only (Fig. 83). Good management dictates non-use of those ranges, especially by cattle, for a three- or four-week period during the bud stage, and until a near mature stage of development (Fig. 84).

Fig. 83. When in bloom, sand shinnery oak is very toxic to livestock, especially cattle that relish the tender new growth. Three or four weeks deferment during the bloom stage and until new leaves are near fully developed is the only safe grazing management. (Photo courtesy U.S. Soil Conservation Service, Texas.)

Of no less importance is the place for seasonal use in management where more productive and efficient use of desirable forage plants will result. Some of the best range plants tend to improve in palatability and nutritive value with maturity. Others respond almost directly the opposite as they reach maturity. This can be important to good productive management of a range. Hairy grama and side-oats grama, on some sites and in some climates, improve with maturity. Therefore, they become a grazing choice in the latter part of the growing season. Under these conditions, a pasture supporting these grasses in abundance is well-suited to fall use, thus, a rather definite season of use. Some of the coarse-stemmed, tall grasses, such as the bluestems, switchgrass, and Indiangrass, may become less desirable for grazing with maturity. Not only are they coarse, stemmy, and hard to graze, but they lose their nutritive quality rather quickly after maturity.

Fig. 84. A pasture deferred during the oak bloom stage. Note the vigor of grass plants in response to this rest period each year, along with proper stocking. (Photo courtesy U.S. Soil Conservation Service, Texas.)

These, and many other seasonal forage plants, occur among the multitude of range plants over the country. Each and every situation may be unique to a particular environment. But nonetheless, they are significant to the most appropriate range management for an area.

TERRAIN INFLUENCES SEASONAL GRAZING

Grazing habits of livestock become one of the stronger influences in grazing management. It must be reckoned with in consideration of grazing management systems, kinds and classes of livestock, age of animals, condition of the range, and even seasonal fluctuations in climate and forage production. It is an established fact that animals will let a habitual pattern of grazing influence their use of the range

Fig. 85. Grass is more plentiful on the steep mountain side than in the smooth valley. But the valley is more easily grazed, therefore only seasonal use is made of the steep site, or when nothing is left to graze in the valley.

to the extent of depriving themselves of their essential body needs. This, of course, will happen only when they are getting their daily fill, even though of poor quality feed.

Although grazing habits may be a result of a combination of factors, terrain of the range is one of the strongest. Livestock, like man, prefer the line of least resistance in achieving even their minimum requirements for existence. They therefore graze areas or range sites that are most accessible, smooth, free of obstructions, and easily grazed. To use such areas, they will often sacrifice quality of forage, time required to get their fill, and travel distance rather than use a more difficult part of the range. Thus, the management of such areas in conjunction with other, more difficult parts of the range becomes a problem of importance to a grazing management plan.

Although the terrain of a country does influence livestock grazing preference, seldom does it completely exclude all grazing use. An exception might be inaccessible or waste land areas. As a rule, areas of distinctly different terrain will have corresponding differences as

Fig. 86. The high lime content of this steep, rocky site makes it attractive to livestock, especially sheep. The hill site is more heavily used than is the valley site.

to kinds and quality of forage plants. But there are instances where adjacent sites of smooth and steep, rough terrain will have plants of nearly the same grazing quality, that is, of about the same nutritive quality and the same period of palatability. This condition will require nothing short of managing facilities, such as fencing, to restrain use of the more favorable terrain if it is not to be overused. But seldom is this practical and actually done.

Often, the area of steep, rough terrain will be supporting a stand of forage plants that have a distinct palatability and nutritive quality period. Examples of such range sites are found in almost any mountainous or hilly area. Shallow, rocky, or gravelly soils often prevail on ridges, hillsides, and mountain slopes. Such ranges of the southwest will normally support good stands of sideoats grama, hairy grama, green sprangletop, bluestems on north and east slopes, along with good amounts of blue and black grama (Fig. 85). Although these ranges have a good variety of grasses and potentially a long grazing season, by preference they are normally grazed seasonally. Following a normally heavy use period of smoother slopes during winter months, a short spring season of use will be made of the rough terrain. Early growth and fresh feed are usually the enticing factors for use of rough sites at that time. But a more likely period for using rough terrain by choice is in the fall of the year. This is primarily a matter of quality of forage with maturity, which also enhances palatability, especially with some species common to mountain ranges.

Other examples of areas in which terrain influences a seasonal pattern of use is where fertility or soil nutrients are directly associated with terrain (Fig. 86). It is not uncommon to find range sites where terrain is directly influenced by the parent material from which the soil was formed. As a result, there is an abundant supply of some one or more mineral elements important to livestock body maintenance and production. Calcium is perhaps the most common element, but many of the so-called trace elements are found with these properties. These nutrient differences seem to be more pronounced and seasonally significant on rough terrain than on smooth country.

TEMPERATURE AND INSECT PESTS INFLUENCE SEASONAL USE

Atmospheric temperatures influence where and when livestock will graze. To ignore these natural instincts in grazing management will normally be reflected in livestock production.

Livestock will seek areas that are most comfortable to them. Such areas may vary with daytime and nighttime temperatures. This is especially true with sheep, but applies to all kinds of domestic livestock to a degree.

As a general rule, livestock will stay in rough country during cold winter months for the added protection afforded. In contrast, they will seek the more open and perhaps higher altitude areas during the hot season, to take advantage of a cooling breeze or wind currents.

Naturally, there will be degrees of variation from hot to cold weather that will affect seasonal changes as to grazing preference areas. These variations may be distinct, or livestock may assume a more gradual change in areas of use. But the alert grazing manager will be able to know these variations on his own range and can provide for seasonal adjustments in management that will be beneficial to both the range and the livestock.

Obvious examples of seasonal use of ranges influenced by temperature are areas with brushy or woody protection and rough broken country in contrast to more open ranges. These differences usually dictate practical seasonal use and management.

The problem of insects detrimental to livestock is closely associated with temperature influence on seasonal use and management of ranges. Although not confined to wooded or brushy sites, blood-sucking insects are bothersome on those sites of southern ranges. Mosquitoes are particularly troublesome under these conditions, as well as near swampy or water areas. Insect-free areas on such ranges are not always possible, but to the extent it is possible, seasonal use management is quite appropriate.

A widespread condition of this kind is the vast areas of range-land where various species of juniper is found in moderate to dense stands (Fig. 87). In association with the temperature factor in these areas is the cedar fly. During the season (summer) this fly becomes prevalent, livestock, particularly cattle and horses, will not stay in such areas unless confined there. When restrained in cedar country, grazing is almost prohibitive especially in daylight hours. Loss of weight, even in young suckling animals, is inevitable.

The cedar fly and the mosquito, along with high-temperature prob-

Fig. 87. A broken terrain heavily infested with juniper provides excellent protection during winter months. But in the summer, heat and insect pests are too severe for stock to stay in such areas. (Photo courtesy U.S. Soil Conservation Service, Texas.)

lems, are so great in some ranching areas that a sound grazing management program is difficult to apply. Seasonal use and adjustments are often basic to any appropriate management plan.

With sheep, and to a lesser extent with other kinds of livestock, the selection of a cool bedground sometimes poses a problem in grazing management, though it is usually restricted to areas of higher elevation within the grazing unit. Usually, the areas affected are low hills and ridges. They become the common bedground perhaps for the entire flock during most or all of the growing season. As a result, sizable areas become both grazed out and trampled out to the extent of near complete ruin. The practical solution to this problem is one of seasonal management, including periodic rest periods of the grazing unit.

KINDS OF LIVESTOCK, GRAZING HABITS, AND SEASONAL USE

The kind and the class of livestock and their grazing preference and habits are often closely allied with seasonal use of various kinds of range. Such use may be an advantage in management of the range, or it may be detrimental. Nevertheless, it is a factor that cannot be overlooked in the interest of maintaining or improving a range.

Different kinds of livestock, including foraging game animals, have their preference of range plants to fulfill their diet needs. These requirements vary from good quality grasses to good quality forbs to annual weeds and even browse and woody plants. Not only availability but palatability and nutritive quality of these categories of range plants are seasonal. Some have rather narrow limits of seasonal preference, while others have almost unlimited seasonal preferences by one or more groups of animals.

It is important to relate these seasons of preference to the grazing use being made of the range. Where the differences in livestock preference are distinct, like the choice of brushy ranges by goats and game animals such as deer, management decisions are not too difficult. However, where preferences may change within the season or year by a single kind or class of animals, seasonal adjustments become important. Or where normally expected changes of preference fail to materialize, seasonal adjustments may again become important.

To illustrate, sheep may be using a major portion of a range in a

Fig. 88. In late summer, livestock have left the vast areas of rough country and concentrated on the deep soil swales and talus slopes. Although it was only for a short season, these areas were overstocked, resulting in complete destruction of this site.

moderate, well-distributed pattern of grazing. They are making good use of a wide variety of both good and low quality plants that are all seasonally palatable. This fact indicates the desirability of a full or possibly a concentrated stocking rate for that season. Then at a given time, perhaps because of a light frost or a critical exhaustion of soil moisture, the palatability or nutritive quality of those plants suddenly drops. The entire animal population immediately moves to other sites or areas in the grazing unit that may represent only a very small portion of the unit (Fig. 88). Within a short time, unless timely seasonal adjustments are made to prevent overuse, damage to that area can occur.

Another common fallacy in grazing management is the instinct of breeding animals with their offspring (Fig. 89). A mother animal will provide the best care possible for her young, even to the extent of sacrificing her own wellbeing on overused or naturally low producing range areas.

During the period of very young offspring, mother animals will select the most accessible, smooth, yet protective site. There they will remain until such time as the young can navigate other, more remote, inaccessible, and rugged areas of the range. It is important, therefore, that such areas of the range be properly reserved for that critical season of the ranching operation.

Fig. 89. Mother animals will sacrifice grazing quality to keep their offspring on a more favored site. Comfort and protection for the young is the first concern. (Photo courtesy U.S. Soil Conservation Service, Texas.)

In any ranching area there will be livestock characteristics that are dependent on or affect seasonal use of portions of the range. Although ranching operations will be somewhat intensified, appropriate seasonal adjustments should be made to both meet the needs of the livestock and at the same time insure protection to the range.

HOW SEASONAL USE INFLUENCES MANAGEMENT

Seasonal use of rangeland may seem to be an innovation of great complexity with which to burden the rancher. This is an erroneous concept and should be considered only in the light of a practical application of a basic principle established, in the first place, by grazing animals. It is only through close observation of their grazing preferences that proper seasonal use of various segments of a range can be known.

It is logical to recognize the fact that where preference, both as to use and non-use of segments of a range, is indicated by animals using the range, the areas involved become focal points in a grazing management program. That is to say, beginning and ending periods of use or non-use in a management plan should coincide, to the extent possible, with livestock grazing preferences.

Seldom will there be instances whereby the grazing of an entire pasture or by an entire herd will fit in perfect harmony with a plan based on seasonal preference alone. Therefore, such a plan may require merely adjustments in livestock management at those periods of grazing preference changes. Also, sacrifices to areas within a pasture may be necessary in the interest of getting near full productive use of the pasture.

To illustrate these kinds of adjustments, let us consider a pasture with a bottomland site comprising two per cent of the entire pasture. In its present condition there is an excessive spring growth of a cool season grass, such as *Stipa sp.* or western wheatgrass. In addition, there is an abundance of palatable annual weeds and grasses, all of which are choice grazing for a time. During the spring and early summer season, this area alone can support twice the number of animals the whole pasture would support all the rest of the year. Therefore, at the beginning of this seasonal production, perhaps double the normal yearlong stocking rate of the entire pasture is in order (Fig. 90).

During this season of use, tremendous gains in livestock weights will no doubt result. Furthermore, use will be made of a forage resource that will be wasted with only the yearlong proper stocking rate for the pasture. Also, this concentrated use will prevent an excess accumulation of vegetation to interfere with forage production the remainder of that season or in subsequent years. Therefore, several prime objectives will have been achieved by heavy seasonal use of that portion of the pasture.

With this kind of use and as the season advances, the vegetation of this site will begin to mature with a loss in both palatability and nutritive quality. As a result, the livestock will disperse to other areas of the pasture in search of better feed. To leave double the normal rate of stocking would be detrimental to the entire pasture. Therefore, this would be the time to adjust the stocking rate of the pasture in line with proper use of the entire pasture.

From the management point of view, steps outlined in the above

Fig. 90. With an abundance of early spring growth of palatable forage, annual or perennial, a heavier than normal stocking rate should be used to make proper and efficient use of that production. (Photo courtesy U.S. Soil Conservation Service, Texas.)

illustration would be beneficial to both livestock production and range management. Yet, the operation is not without some inconveniences and sacrifices. In the first place, movement of all or a part of the livestock would be necessary at two times, the beginning and the end of the seasonal use period. Also, continued use of the particular site involved, even by only half the number of animals, could result in overuse of perhaps the most productive site in the pasture. This is a sacrifice, but it need not be too serious. Other management practices, such as a rest period, could be utilized at a crucial time to compensate for what might have otherwise been permanent damage to that site.

With a practical knowledge of both livestock and range management as pertaining to a ranching operation, all needed facets of a good range management plan can be carried out with comparative ease, but not without due consideration of all phases of the operation. Pastures can usually be paired to provide needed use and rest periods. Due consideration of livestock needs, often by kinds and classes, can be fitted into a grazing management plan that embodies needed seasonal use and rest periods. Once such a plan of management has been developed, carrying it out can become routine, and, above all, flexible enough to provide for needed adjustments as they arise.

RANCH IMPROVEMENTS TO FACILITATE SEASONAL USE

As a general rule, ranch improvements to facilitate the handling and management of livestock and proper management of the range are not extensively made. Most ranches have been improved to the satisfaction of the operator. However, with improved knowledge, more intensive care and management of both livestock and the range are becoming important. As a result, facilities for meeting these intensities are being provided.

As improvements are planned, those providing for seasonal use of

Fig. 91. Fencing out a small pasture made possible profitable seasonal use of this salt grass area at a time when it was badly needed and when it was a preference to the livestock.

Fig. 92. A temporary water location will make a seasonal use area available at a time when profitable use can be made of it. (Photo courtesy U.S. Soil Conservation Service, Texas.)

specific areas of the range should be given high priority. Usually provision for this and other range management needs can be provided at little or no extra expense.

In this regard, fencing arrangements can often be such that areas with a particular seasonal grazing value can be in a single pasture (Fig. 91). This may involve the fencing of certain range sites into grazing units that would facilitate management in many ways other than seasonal use.

Other improvements that can facilitate seasonal use are the location and control of water developments. A water location that is accessible to an area of seasonal use for best management may be used either to encourage or discourage use of the area (Fig. 92). This, of course, is achieved by making water available to animals using the area, or by closing it off, forcing them to other water locations.

The placement of salt either near or away from areas needing controlled use is also helpful. However, it should be kept in mind that the control of livestock by any method other than fencing or herding may not be completely accomplished. Animals will travel excessive distances to a choice grazing area. They will also travel farther than normal away from a less desirable area. It is the latter fact that often disrupts needed seasonal or concentrated use of areas that are not a first choice by the kind of livestock using the range.

As a general rule, ranch improvements to provide for seasonal use are more feasible on small ranching operations than on large operations.

Chapter 11

DISTRIBUTION OF GRAZING IN RANGE MANAGEMENT

Achieving proper grazing use of all the range by distribution of grazing. Management considerations to this basic principle. Type of vegetation as determined by range sites, and i†s influence on distribution of grazing. Accessibility, roughness, kind of vegetation, and kind of livestock related to terrain of a range and grazing distribution. The influences of temperature, snowfall, and rainfall on grazing in various climates. Selective grazing by kinds and classes of livestock.

Distribution of grazing is another of the important basic principles in managing rangeland; it is closely allied with seasonal use, and is, in fact, a tool in achieving proper use of the range. As the term implies, it is a phase of grazing management that insures all of a range, including all grazable plants, is used uniformly without overuse of any part of the range except possibly sacrifice areas.

Distribution of grazing can be a problem wherever rangelands are involved, and since reasons for this problem may vary from one area to another, solutions also vary. As a general rule, however, both the problem and the solution are less acute in areas of large operations and uniform country. At least, under these conditions, the range manager has more opportunity to do something about both the problem and the solution. Grazing distribution becomes complex on ranges with diverse topography and vegetation. Here, grazing instincts of livestock have to be relied on more intensively to cope with needed seasonal adjustments. In general, small ranches and small pastures do not present a problem of distribution of grazing. Livestock confined to comparatively small areas will cover the entire area too often, regardless of their preferences.

MANAGEMENT CONSIDERATIONS FOR DISTRIBUTION OF GRAZING

Poor distribution of grazing on rangeland is caused by many factors. Some are natural, and some are more or less man made. But with proper consideration of range and livestock management, ranch improvements, and in some instances, land treatment, good grazing distribution can be had.

The natural influences that affect grazing distribution are: type of vegetation, terrain, climate, selectivity of grazing, and livestock habits. Man made influences include: size and shape of pastures, location of range facilities such as water and salt locations, and kind, class, and management of livestock.

Although the optimum degree of grazing may not be possible on each and every kind of range forage, better use can certainly be made of it when all factors of management are taken into account. It is important to make more use of what might normally be underused plants, and at the same time not to overuse the better plants. This is the objective in achieving the proper distribution of grazing on a range.

TYPE OF VEGETATION INFLUENCES DISTRIBUTION

The different vegetation types that may be found on a range often adversely influence the grazing pattern of livestock. Ranges not severely deteriorated will have inherent variations in vegetation caused by soil differences, topographic differences, or both. Differences in vegetation types may create a season of use problem as well as a distribution of grazing problem. Regardless of the immediate influence on grazing use, the result is the same. It is a matter of where, when, and for how long a given area is used and what plants are being grazed. However, from the standpoint of practical management, it is important to recognize which of the two principles of grazing management—distribution or seasonal selectivity—is being violated. If seasonal selectivity is the real problem, it may be for a short duration only; whereas if it is a distribution problem, the reason may be of a rather permanent nature. In either instance, the principle of grazing distribution is being hampered. In finding a solution, the severity of the problem must be evaluated and appropriate adjustments made.

Fig. 93. A desert shrub type with little if any perennial grass is seldom grazed except following a rain to start weeds and improve the palatability of a few shrubs. At that time it is important to apply the principle of proper use.

Because of the dual principles of management involved where different vegetation types occur within a grazing unit, it is logical to apply a common treatment of management to the fullest possible extent (Fig. 93). That is, to insure proper use of such areas, the season of selectivity with appropriate adjustments in the grazing load will be necessary. Other than seasonal selectivity, control of the livestock onto or off such areas by fencing or herding may have to be provided.

Although the quality of forage by vegetation types is the primary factor in regulating use, it is not necessarily the only influencing factor. Terrain and accessibility may be a deterrent to use of some vegetation types on a range. Location of improperly used vegetation sites with respect to livestock management facilities will affect distribution of grazing. When left to the animal, the quality of range forage has the strongest influence of any factors related to grazing distribution. By instinct for survival and reproduction, the best feed that can be reached will be selected, even at the expense of production. In range management, the objective is to make available this highest quality feed, at the time and in amounts sufficient for efficient production of both range forage and livestock products.

TERRAIN AND GRAZING DISTRIBUTION

The terrain has much to do with how a range is used. Generally, with topographic features ranging from smooth to rough or extremely rough, grazing use can be measured by degrees. The smoother country will be used first and the most because of the ease of grazing. As the country becomes increasingly rough, steep, and rocky, the degree of use will normally be less. But as a measure of use of the range, the degree to which the increasingly rough country is used is a valuable indicator to the range manager. When there is a choice of range sites, such areas will be selected for use for two reasons: seasonal palatability and nutritional quality; decline of the grazing quality of the more accessible sites (Fig. 94). This, of course, would be further indicated by a lowered range condition of the sites of smoother terrain.

In management, the factor of accessibility or inaccessibility as an influence on distribution of grazing becomes an important criterion to use of the range. As related to the kind or class of livestock, this factor can be a reliable indicator of range use and range condition.

Fig. 94. In this type of country, without grazing distribution control for better use of the rough country, the flats and valleys will be grazed to a lower range condition than the mountains.

Fig. 95. Terrain had no influence on the heavily grazed sheep range at left. The cattle range on the right is heavily grazed on the lower slopes, but lightly grazed on the steep slopes, even in a dry year. (Photo courtesy U.S. Soil Conservation Service, Texas.)

Accessibility is a varying factor, in that areas that are preferred by one kind or class of livestock may be a last choice or even a forced use area by another class of animals (Fig. 95).

Poor distribution of grazing due to terrain of the country has several alternative solutions. A solution of first importance should be based on seasonal selective use of different areas of the terrain. This is predicated on the concept that site selection is a logical and a freely used pattern of grazing by the kind of livestock using the range. This permits timely adjustments in the grazing load to achieve proper use of the area or areas involved. This same consideration is required for both types of grazing areas—the one receiving infrequent use (the rough area), and the one that carries the bulk of the grazing load throughout a major portion of the year (the smoother area).

If selective use adjustments are not feasible, other grazing control practices may be appropriate, such as fencing for controlled management, or herding if it is appropriate for the type of operation involved. The development of strategically located water facilities may be used to pull livestock into areas of rough terrain (Fig. 96). This, in turn, necessitates control and exclusion from use of other water facilities accessible to nearby areas of smoother terrain.

The placement of salt or mineral supplements in areas of rough terrain may also induce more grazing use of them. However, the placement of salt or water locations as a means of livestock control and range use cannot be fully relied upon to completely achieve this objective. Livestock can and will travel long distances to water. But these practices can be considered a helpful tool, and, in some instances, are all that is needed. When they can be related to seasonal selectivity of use, much can be accomplished.

Another alternative that has merit is that of the kind of livestock best suited to parts of the range not being fully utilized (Fig. 97). Even a change in the class of livestock may be beneficial and profitable. When changes in the kind or class of livestock seem to be a practical solution, consideration should be given the total range resource. Is the entire range suited to a single kind or class of livestock? Or is there a place for mixed kinds and classes to be profitably handled to gain better distribution of grazing and use of the entire range? These are decisions for the ranch operator to make with full concern and consideration for getting full and proper use of his range, along with economical production.

CLIMATIC INFLUENCES ON DISTRIBUTION OF GRAZING

Distribution of grazing over a range may be directly influenced by climate. Temperature changes are the primary factor. However, snowfall in mountainous areas and excessive rainfall, particularly on coastal ranges, incur distinct limitations to grazing.

Three distinct fluctuations are important to grazing management: snowfall that precludes the use of some mountain ranges during winter months and thus dictates use of ranges of lower elevations during that period; short seasonal fluctuations in use as a result of climatic influences on the quality of the forage; and day to day and night temperature variations that cause livestock to be selective in their pattern of grazing. This is usually associated with temperature

Fig. 96. This water storage supplied by pipe line and booster power makes possible better use of rough country and areas far removed from accessible water supplies.

Fig. 97. Mutton goats are the best kind of livestock to make efficient use of poorly watered, steep, rough country.

and air movement at higher elevation, as compared with low elevations, and often tree or shrub infested areas.

These influences are important in both hot weather and cold weather. When it is hot, more use will be made of higher elevations that are cooled by air currents. When it is cold, a reverse pattern will prevail, and protection from cooler temperatures will be afforded in the low land areas. Sometimes these areas of choice may be comparatively small, yet, because of temperature influence, they are grazed for a much greater portion of time than the size would justify.

Too much rainfall is seldom a problem on rangeland. However, on coastal ranges excessive rainfall, high temperatures, and insects combine to affect the grazing pattern. When these conditions prevail, stock will, to the extent possible, move to higher ground. Although there may be only slight difference in elevations, the differences may be that of water filled potholes or even surface coverage of water as compared to no more than a wet surface soil. Slight though they may be, these differences have an influence on distribution of grazing on these ranges.

SELECTIVE GRAZING AND DISTRIBUTION

Next to numbers of livestock using a range, selective grazing has a greater influence on grassland management than any other controllable use factor. Even before domestic livestock began using the range, selective grazing by buffalo, deer, antelope, and other foraging game animals controlled where they would graze at various seasons. The kind of vegetation, seasonal palatability, accessibility, terrain and climatic influences were the factors that dictated selective use. Because of their lack of restraint, animals were at liberty to move about over vast areas, to graze where forage was most plentiful and nutritious. With such freedom of choice, they naturally evaded any area that did not meet their needs. Thereby, areas once used, possibly too closely, were not used again until they had recovered to near full production capacity. Thus, with few exceptions such as areas near water, the entire range country was allowed to maintain itself through natural processes of plant maintenance, as permitted by good distribution of grazing.

These same natural instincts of grazing prevail among all kinds of domestic livestock. They all continue to select the best area of forage available to them. A primary difference has been limitations of movement from one area to another by property ownership and fencing. Such confinement has resulted in repeat usage of favored grazing areas, usually all too frequently and certainly before normal and full recovery had taken place.

For one or more logical reasons, within almost any grazing unit are those areas of preference. Nearness to a water location, or other facilities for the handling and management of livestock, is perhaps a primary factor influencing selective use. This would be closely followed by those areas that are accessible and most easily grazed. As a rule, under normal ranching operations, they will be the most heavily used and very likely will be in the poorest range condition, and currently the least productive portions of the ranch. This is true, in spite of their being the most productive lands on the ranch, such as valley sites that are usually most accessible and most easily grazed.

Because of accessibility and ease of grazing, obtaining uniform distribution of grazing over the rest of the range is often made more difficult. For the best and perhaps the most practical results, a system of rotation deferment is a first choice in management. Simple deferment during the growing season, or at least every other growing season, is good management if the area is not destructively grazed following the deferment. Another alternative is adjustments in numbers of animals during periods of concentrated selective use of significant areas in a pasture. Such adjustments would have to conform to the grazing capacity of the selected areas and for the period of preference use. Often this amount of livestock manipulation is not practical.

RANCH IMPROVEMENTS AND GRAZING DISTRIBUTION

Ranch improvements may or may not contribute to the principle of grazing distribution. Seldom is that principle given specific consideration when a ranch is being improved. Fortunately, a majority of ranching operations, with whatever improvements are at hand, can be planned for grazing management that will conform reasonably well with good distribution of grazing.

The location, size, and shape of a pasture, and possibly direction of prevailing livestock travel, can be important to grazing distribution. A pasture that includes many and varied range sites is a difficult one in which to achieve uniform grazing throughout. The problems encountered in obtaining uniform distribution of grazing use from a multiple site grazing unit encourages the size and layout of a pasture on the most uniform type of country possible. At best, there will ordinarily be management problems just to meet the needs of minor site variations.

Obviously, the larger the pasture the more freedom of choice of grazing areas there will be. That is, the more nearly a pasture can resemble an unfenced range, the less concentrated grazing pressure there will be on various range sites. In contrast, the smaller the pasture, the less selectivity of preference sites there will be, and at the same time, the greater will be the possibility for it to be uniform as to range sites. However, fencing as a solution to a grazing distribution problem often is not feasible in conformity with other management factors and costs involved. When fencing is not feasible, then other facets of grazing management need to be resorted to in order to get the most uniform distribution of grazing possible.

Next in importance to fencing (Fig. 98), water locations, supplemented with salt and mineral locations are the most important ranch improvement as a regulator of grazing distribution. Water strategically located is important to any grazing distribution and uniformity of grazing.

Although water locations are important, a word of caution is necessary. More water locations or closer spacing of them is not always helpful. This might actually contribute to overuse of the range by increased concentration of the livestock.

Although livestock will travel great distances for water, this is not in the best interest of either the animal or the range. Travel time and distance take away from grazing and resting time. Energy used in excessive travel takes away from production by the animal. And, if water is too far removed from the grazing area, going to water will be delayed as long as possible, to the further detriment of animal production.

Misplaced or too widely spaced water locations cause undesirable grazing patterns. If animals have too far to travel between water and suitable grazing areas, the pattern of use is that of grazing out and trailing back. As this continues, trails become longer and deeper, making bigger and better water channels to carry rainfall off the range and inducing erosion. At the same time, the water location becomes a point of concentration with destructive grazing of every-

Fig. 98. This stock pond is located near an area of rough, Permean outcrop supporting good grass but seldom used because of distance to water. The installation greatly improved distribution of grazing over the range.

thing edible. As this continues, a series of concentric rings of progressive degrees of overuse will result. In time, this condition becomes so serious that nothing is left near the water to graze. The grazing pattern then becomes that of trailing to water and trailing back to forage to graze.

A logical remedial measure is proper spacing of water with a proper rate of stocking. Proper spacing of water locations depends primarily on the kind of country over which animals have to graze and travel. Travel distances most practical for benefit to both the livestock and the range are as follows: for rough country, ½ mile; for rolling, hilly country, 1 mile; for smooth, flat country, 2 miles; for sandy country, 1½ miles if smooth, and 1 mile if undulating and dunes.

Under any conditions of travel, an exception to the above spacing would be at sites where water is purposely located to induce grazing use of otherwise unused forage. To space water according to a desirable spacing plan would defeat the purpose of that planned treatment.

To insure proper distribution and uniformity of grazing, a range requires both careful management of the range and the livestock. It is more difficult to achieve this particular objective than almost any other phase of range management. This is due primarily to the fact that the livestock have to be managed and manipulated more by persuasion and inducement than by direct control. Whatever the cost and trouble, proper distribution and uniformity of grazing are among the most rewarding achievements in range management. Without them, the loss in production can be twofold. First, there is loss from forage production that would otherwise be unused; second, there is loss through continued overuse and progressive expansion of that part of the range used by choice. Improper distribution of grazing, especially when induced by selective use, becomes a continuing and expanding deterioration of a range. Areas of selectivity continue to grow and eventually will engulf the entire range, resulting in severe overuse and poor condition of all the range.

Chapter 12

KINDS OF LIVESTOCK BEST SUITED TO THE RANGE

Equivalence of range management and livestock management. Compatibility of livestock with the kind of range. Livestock adaptation to specific kinds of rangeland. Influence of kinds of livestock on range management. Range forage preference by kinds of livestock related to terrain, seasonal grazing, distribution of grazing, and stocking rates. Grazing habits and their effect on range utilization, range condition, and range trends.

Three of the cardinal principles of range management have been discussed in previous chapters: Proper Degree of Use, Proper Season of Use, and Proper Distribution of Grazing. The application of each is dependent on the fourth principle, Kind of Livestock Best Suited to The Range. In fact, this is the regulator in the application of all principles. It is only through control of the numbers of animals, where they graze, when, and for how long, that the various facets of range management can be achieved.

Use and management of a range can best be achieved when the kind of livestock is compatible with the range that is available. Before domestic livestock were brought onto western rangelands, game animals using the range selected the habitat best suited to their needs. Inasmuch as domestic livestock will do the same, if given the opportunity, this provides the clue to suitability of the kind of livestock to a kind of range.

Historically, domesticated livestock came from parts of the world that provided their best environment, and characteristics of various kinds of animals adjusted to the environment in which they lived.

Zebu cattle originated in tropical climates. Since becoming domesticated and even highly developed, they are the breed best suited to hot, humid range areas (Fig. 99). Their inherent resistance to insects also contributes to their adaptation to ranges with tropical influences.

In contrast, English breeds of cattle were developed under climates with less intense heat and humidity and are better adapted to climates where these characteristics are less extreme. They have adapted more readily to colder and even drier climates than have breeds of tropical origin (Fig. 100). It should be noted, however, that crossing of various breeds to fit climatic and range characteristics has been an important phase of animal science (Fig. 101). The Santa Gertrudis breed of cattle is an outstanding example of such development (Fig. 102).

Of special significance in animal adaptation to a range is the natural habitat of goats. Goats prefer a rough terrain, since they are able to maneuver over such country, and rough, steep lands usually provide a type of forage palatable and nutritious for them (Fig. 103). A third factor that seems to contribute to this natural adaptation is freedom from excessive competition with other animals in a rough country.

These adaptation factors have identified various range areas as suitable for the production of certain kinds of livestock. For example, the Edwards Plateau of Texas is noted as a sheep country (Fig. 104).

Marsh ranges through the coastal areas of southern states are becoming more important for cattle with Brahman blood, a characteristic essential to satisfactory production. Some breeds, such as shorthorn and angus, have, because of their originating environment, been less suited to ranges of rough terrain than other breeds.

It is important to note that with time, adjustments of adaptation have taken place, altering these original concepts to a considerable degree. Various breeds are becoming "better rustlers" and better users of all kinds of rangelands. And, great progress has been made through the crossbreeding of all kinds of domestic livestock to improve not only livestock production but range adaptation and use.

These factors of habitat and adaptation do not necessarily impose a monopoly on a kind of livestock production. Nor are such areas necessarily limited to a single kind of livestock. Except for a few specific areas, such as those that are extremely rough and near-inaccessible, there are ranges without distinct variations as to kinds of country. To this extent, corresponding variations as to kinds and classes of livestock can be managed with at least a reasonable and practical degree of suitability. Furthermore, these variations in livestock adaptations are important to efficient and economic use of much of the range country.

Fig. 99. Resistance to heat and insects makes Brahman cattle well-adapted to southern ranges. (Photo courtesy U.S. Soil Conservation Service, Louisiana.)

Fig. 100. Hereford cattle have perhaps been the most adaptable of any other breed. They were the foundation of improved cattle operations in the United States. (Photo courtesy U.S. Soil Conservation Service, Texas.)

Fig. 101. Longhorn cattle were the first of the domestic breeds to roam the ranges of our western states.

Fig. 102. Santa Gertrudis cattle, a cross between Brahman and short-horn breeds, can be adapted to many and varied climates and conditions. (Photo courtesy U.S. Soil Conservation Service, Texas.)

Fig. 103. Goats are well-adapted to rough country and have a prefer-ence for the forage plants adapted to that type of range.

Fig. 104. Sheep are especially well-adapted to the rough limestone country of the Edwards Plateau of west central and southwest Texas. (Photo courtesy U.S. Soil Conservation Service, Texas.)

KIND OF LIVESTOCK INFLUENCES RANGE MANAGEMENT

Livestock, being the tool by which any and all facets of range management are carried out, are of equal importance to the range itself. Not only their well-being but also their production must be a prime objective in the complete operation. A frequently expressed objection to the application of range management practices is the disturbance to the livestock involved. Some ranchers cling tenaciously to the idea that every animal on the ranch should have a home of its choice and remain there unmolested. Others, however, have become receptive to manipulation of livestock for improved range management and are just as firm in their convictions of benefits to be had.

There are a number of livestock characteristics that have specific influences on range management. Some of the most significant are: range forage preference by kinds of livestock; influence of terrain on the kind of livestock that uses the range; grazing distribution by kinds of livestock; effect of the kind of livestock on seasonal use of the range; the manner in which livestock graze; and the relationship between kinds of livestock and range condition.

Although these factors and influences have rather general application, there are many details that are significant to local situations. These details may be related specifically to the vegetation, terrain, or soil characteristics of the range. They may pertain not only to kinds of livestock but also to classes, size, ages, or even breeds of animals. Consideration of game animals that use the range is highly important in any management consideration (Fig. 105).

FORAGE PREFERENCE BY KINDS OF LIVESTOCK

All foraging animals eat grass and other types of forage plants. But the important concern in range management is that there are differences in the choice of plants taken by different kinds of animals. "By choice" means that when there is a sufficiently wide variety of plants, a preference is available. It would be much better for both the range and the livestock if the choice could be made from the best plants that would ever be found on the range. Unfortunately, this is seldom possible to the fullest extent, due to range deterioration through the years. Therefore, because of variations in range

Fig. 105. A kind of country that is widely diversified as to kinds of livestock suited to it. Here blacktail deer make considerable use of the range and must be accounted for in management.

condition, animal choices have to be made of the plants that are there. Under these conditions it becomes a detail of management to determine which plants are being taken, when, by what kind or class of livestock, and for how long they are selected.

Even though livestock forage preferences are many and varied, a general guide to overall preference should be helpful. Information based on experience and limited research is indicative of the preference major kinds of domestic livestock will make of broadly classified range plants. This information is given in Table 3.

TABLE 3

Grazing Choice of Range Plants

by Kinds of Domestic Livestock (In Per Cent)

KIND OF PLANTS	HORSES	CATTLE	SHEEP	GOATS
Grass	90	70	60	20
Weeds	4	20	30	20
Browse	6	10	10	60

In grazing management it is not enough to merely identify the kind of livestock with these broad categories of range plants. Within each of these groups of plants are many choices and rejections made by various kinds of animals using the range. Even among the grasses, there will be those species that are objectionable to cattle and horses even though grass is their preference forage. And in the other categories of plants will be many that are objectionable, even to sheep and goats with their strong preference for plants other than grasses.

Although livestock choices of the major groups of plants are important, the choice that will be made of plants within a single group by various kinds and classes of animals is of perhaps equal importance. To illustrate, horses and mature cattle will make far greater use of a coarse stem grass than will sheep, goats, or even young cattle. Also, the season or stage of development of one grass, as compared to another, will have different degrees of preference by different kinds of livestock. The same can be said for the many different kinds of weeds and brush species that occupy much of the range country. As an example, consider the conditions that prevailed in west central Texas following a severe drought period from 1932, and which extended well into 1936. With the advent of above-normal rainfall in the fall of 1936, there came a luxuriant spring growth of weeds of exceptionally high palatability and quality for both cattle and sheep. These included such species as huisache daisy, woolly and redseed plantain, Texas and California filaree, and milkvetch. Both cattle and sheep thrived on this forage during the spring and early summer, an important production period for offspring. But on the other side of the ledger, not only was this a seasonal resource that was quickly dissipated with maturity, but the abundant growth of this production adversely affected struggling perennial grasses because of excessive competition. With fixed stocking rates this type of forage production, coupled with a season long grazing pattern, only contributed to continued range deterioration. In subsequent years, not only were desirable grasses further depleted, but these better weeds were also gradually replaced by those less palatable, especially to cattle. Of most importance in this latter category were such weeds as annual broomweed, and bitterweed, both of which are unpalatable and the latter even poisonous (Fig. 106 and 107).

Because of differences in livestock preference for forage plants, the consideration of more than a single kind of livestock often becomes important to good management. This may be desirable on a year-

Fig. 106. An invasion of annual broomweed following a drought period. By emerging in the fall or early spring, these weeds are strongly competitive to weakened grass plants in early stages of spring growth. (Photo courtesy U.S. Soil Conservation Service, Texas.)

Fig. 107. On severely depleted ranges, poisonous plants such as bitterweed are strong invaders. Control is expensive by any method; aerial application of chemical sprays is very effective when properly applied. (Photo courtesy U.S. Soil Conservation Service, Texas.)

long basis as a permanent type of operation, or the situation may be more applicable on a seasonal basis. In either instance it is termed multiple-purpose ranges and multiple-type livestock operation.

As an example of the significance of multiple-type operations, consider the Edwards Plateau of Texas. It is a country capable of supporting good stands of a wide variety of desirable range grasses. In addition, these grasslands are interspersed with liveoak and other desirable browse-type plants. (This is the current condition, having evolved from a grass-tree savannah by an increase in tree and underbrush growth.) With good rainfall, an abundance of winter and early spring weeds may be expected, many of which are choice feed for sheep. This makes a range with a wide variety of forage plants, well-suited to the production of three kinds of livestock: cattle, sheep, and goats. This is the type of operation common to much of that area at present. However, the successful ranchers in the area are those who use both browse and weed production by sheep and goats to supplement grass utilization by all three kinds of livestock. They use the degree of grazing of their better grasses as the key to the utilization of their ranges. This is contrary to the original concept, that stocking rates with multiple kinds of livestock could be increased to the extent of available weeds and browse without injury to the stand of desirable grasses.

KIND OF LIVESTOCK AS INFLUENCED BY TERRAIN

Reference has already been made to the general adaptation of kinds of livestock to the terrain of the country. Aside from the general characterization of such adaptations as goats to rough country, sheep to dry areas of limited water supplies, and zebu cattle to tropic-like environments, livestock can generally be adapted to the terrain of most range country. Such a generalization, however, becomes obscure when it comes to the details of a good range management plan where distinct variations in terrain occur on a given ranch. These major range-livestock adaptations to specific kinds of terrain may seem insignificant, but they are important in an overall plan of management for ranches located in regions other than these specific kinds of country.

Many ranches of predominately smooth to rolling topography have areas of rough country. There are ranches where the topography includes productive grassland types at higher elevations, with adjacent desert-like range at a lower elevation. Southern ranges may be of both upland and swamp-like range types. The kind of livestock becomes important where these various kinds of range occur. As a general guide, however, the kind of livestock best suited would be that with tolerance to the most stringent factors of production. Such limitations would logically have to apply to enough of the ranch to be significant to management and production.

Management considerations for these various topographic areas on a ranch of necessity include seasonal use and distribution of grazing as well as the kind of livestock best suited. Of course, the degree of grazing over all the range, regardless of the terrain, is a final limitation of the grazing management plan. Even when only minor restrictions of accessibility and livestock movement over the area are imposed by terrain, variations as to kinds of vegetation on these sites are the management factor involved. These differences may be such that the kind of livestock would have a direct influence on management and production.

These influencing factors of terrain have a close relationship to diversified ranching, that is, diversification as to kinds of livestock. There may be varying degrees of diversification, including two or more kinds of livestock, or a diversity as to classes of animals within a single kind. Cattle, sheep, and goats is perhaps the most common mixture of livestock. Sheep and goats are a very compatible combination where their preferred types of range occur on a ranch.

When different kinds of livestock do not provide a desired type of operation, breeding animals in combination with stocker animals can be managed together conveniently and efficiently. It is recognized that steers and mutton sheep or goats will travel farther, and graze over more country and over rough country, by choice, much more than will mother stock with young.

KIND OF LIVESTOCK AND DISTRIBUTION OF GRAZING

Different grazing habits, different preferences of range forage, and different kinds of country preferred by various kinds and classes of livestock, become an important tool in getting proper distribution of grazing. Knowing these characteristics of animals is important in the knowledge and experience of the range manager. He must know not only the kind of range preferred but the choice and seasonal preference of the more important forage plants of each type of range.

Equipped with this information, the range manager may increase the carrying capacity of a range by the use of the kinds of livestock that will more uniformly distribute themselves over the range. Here again, the kinds of country to which various kinds and classes of livestock are best suited becomes important. But, of even greater importance is management to insure coverage of all the range and proper use of all kinds of suitable forage that is available. This can be achieved most satisfactorily by use of the kinds of livestock that will, of their own instinct, follow such a pattern of grazing use.

Differences in kinds of range forage, especially on a single range site or kind of country, very often impose a range use and management problem. An example is a mixed grass and browse range, each making up about equal amounts of forage. Here a single kind of livestock will overuse one kind of forage and underuse the other, because of feeding preference. On the other hand, by a proper proportion of two or possibly three kinds of animals, proper use and added production can be had from that range.

Other examples of poor distribution of grazing that can be improved by use of the right kind of livestock are distance of travel from water to grazing areas, size of the pasture, spacing of water and salt locations, and the existing range condition. Desirable grazing areas may be farther from a point of concentration, such as water, than breeding animals with young will travel. Nonbreeding animals will extend their area of grazing to such areas and beyond in their normal grazing pattern. Also, a grazing characteristic of horses to travel directly to and from water, often on the run, will insure better distribution of grazing of far-off areas in a pasture.

KIND OF LIVESTOCK AND SEASONAL USE

Seasonal preference of range forage by various kinds and classes of livestock is generally not as significant to range management as other practices and principles. There are, however, situations whereby seasonal production and use of a range are important to one kind of livestock but of little value to other kinds. This usually involves areas of a range type of considerable size and of uniform composition of the vegetation. In the southwest are vast areas of grasses that have

Fig. 108. A clay flat site producing a pure stand of tobosagrass. The most production can be had from this range by mature cattle in the spring and early summer months.

rather coarse and harsh stem and foliage production with distinct seasons of choice grazing. Tobosa grass, and, to a lesser degree, galleta-grass are in this category (Fig. 108). Alkali sacaton is also somewhat restrictive as to its seasonal palatability and nutritive quality. These grasses, which usually dominate one or more range sites, can best be utilized by cattle and horses in spring and early summer. Therefore, for maximum production, the ranching operation with these kinds of grasses should include cattle and possibly horses, if they are a profitable enterprise.

Various species of threeawn (*Aristida sp.*), where they may be rather dominant in the composition, will be utilized better by cattle and horses than by sheep and goats. This, coupled with the fact that they usually start spring growth ahead of most other summer grasses, makes a pasture with good amounts of threeawn very desirable for early spring use by cattle. In the southwest, pastures of this type are often used for calving.

In addition to these situations, where a single kind of grass dictates a seasonal use pattern of a range, there are many other forage plants that are seasonal to specific kinds of livestock. The low-growing grass species of hairy tridens, common to the shallow soils of rocky ridges, are particularly attractive to sheep for a short period in the fall. Small dropseeds, some of which are annuals, such as puff sheath and Texas dropseed, are relished by horses in October. Yucca blooms common to southwest ranges are first choice to cattle in early summer. Use of these blooms often furnish sufficient water to satisfy cattle needs for several days at a time.

Throughout the range country are many plants, perhaps locally adapted, that are seasonally attractive to one kind of livestock or another. Although generally not of such importance that grazing management can be based on them, they are a grazing resource that should be utilized to the extent possible. Logically, such use would take into consideration the kind or class of livestock that would make the best use of them.

THE WAY ANIMALS GRAZE INFLUENCES THE DEGREE OF GRAZING USE

No kind or class of livestock has a monopoly on the ability to graze a range too closely. Any and all of them can do a first-class job of it when grazing management is conducive to overuse of the range. There are differences, however, as to how overgrazing is brought about by various kinds of animals.

In addition to the various reasons for livestock being selective in their choice of a grazing area, there are also differences in how animals will roam and travel over the range in grazing. Except for the decided curiosity and roving instinct of goats, the amount of travel in the grazing process is influenced by many factors. Range condition is perhaps the number one regulator of grazing habits. Other factors, such as seasonal palatability, terrain, spacing of water locations, size and shape of the pasture, and age of the animals, all of which have been previously discussed, do influence grazing habits. Of these, no doubt, selectivity of plants has the greatest influence on the way animals graze. Variations in the choice of plants by different kinds of animals and the availability of those plants will usually set the patterns of range use.

The selection of plants to graze is done primarily by the sense of smell. However, palatability is also enhanced by taste buds on the surface of the tongue. Different kinds of livestock seem to have palatability choices peculiar to themselves, along with their preferences as to coarseness, toughness, or roughness of the forage. Nevertheless, plants that are highest in proteins, carbohydrates, and minerals are selected and grazed first. Also, to the extent needed, these same plants may undergo repeat grazing rather often, which may be the beginning of over-grazing the range.

With some kinds of livestock this process of selective grazing results in what is known as spot grazing. This condition often occurs on ranges that have deteriorated to a low condition where better plants for that range occur in colonies or patches. Buffalograss is a good example of this type of use. However, the problem is not confined to low-condition ranges. Even climax ranges, where the higher type grasses occur in colonies, as they often do, tend to encourage spot grazing. An example is big bluestem colonies interspersed in a stand of little bluestem and other climax grasses of the true prairie. When available, big bluestem is nearly always a choice grass.

The grazing equipment of various kinds of animals can make a difference in how plants are grazed.[1] All animals use lips, tongue, and teeth in the grazing process. The lips separate the selected plant from among the several plants that may be growing in a stand. But it is the arrangement of teeth that has most to do with the manner in which a plant is cropped. Ruminating animals, especially cattle, with only lower front teeth working against a toughened pad or gum, graze with a tearing and biting combination. They use the tongue to roll the forage into a bite-size bundle for tearing and biting from the plant. This, of course, is when there is sufficient height of the forage to permit use of the tongue. When the forage is too short for effective use of the tongue, cattle can use their lips and tooth-gum arrangement for close grazing.

In slight contrast to cattle, sheep, goats, deer, and other ruminating animals, make less use of the tongue and more use of the lip and tooth-gum process of grazing. This characteristic enables these animals to graze a range more closely than cattle can. This is important in grazing management systems.

Horses are said to be hard users of the range. This can be attributed partially to their grazing process. The lips are used very effectively to assemble the forage into the mouth. Then both upper and lower incisors, arranged for complete cutting, nip forage at ground level, or at whatever level is necessary for a bite-size quantity. This grazing process, along with severe trampling of the range, is a contributing factor to destructive grazing by horses.

[1] B. W. Allred, *Practical Grassland Management* (1950) .

These and other habits and traits of grazing by various kinds of livestock have a bearing on what happens to range forage. The effects are particularly significant as they influence a downward trend in range condition. As long as the trend is upward, or even static, for the range as a whole, there is little need for concern about grazing patterns or how the grass is cropped.

Of particular importance in range management are the many grazing characteristics of animals that affect the basic principles of management: the degree of grazing, especially of the important forage plants; the seasonal use or selectivity of important plants for any reason; and, the distribution of grazing and uniform use of all the range. It is the relationship between these principles and the livestock that graze the range that determines the ultimate condition of the range. Livestock are perpetrators of range trends either up or down, but not necessarily of their own choosing. When confined by management and control, they make the most efficient use possible of the range to satisfy their body requirements. Their grazing habits and processes are incidental to the influence they have and the response of the range to that use. A knowledge of livestock activities on the range is important if livestock requirements and range management requirements are to be correlated into a successful ranching operation.

Chapter 13

RANGE MANAGEMENT PLANNING

The what and why of a range management plan. Resources of the range basic to a management plan. Identifying resource and management problems. Alternatives and flexibility essential to a ranch plan. Analysis of problems as encountered in each grazing unit or pasture. Recording problem treatment and management needs as encountered. Development of a coordinated plan for the entire ranch. Improvement and management needs correlated with forage resources and the livestock enterprise. Summary of important considerations in ranch planning.

Planning range management is simply a systematic approach to determining what the range problems are, deciding what needs to be done about them, and devising a plan as to what will be done. Such a plan is not workable unless it is correlated with livestock management, range improvement needs, and cost-return benefits to the ranching operation. Who can develop such a plan? Essentially no one other than the ranch operator himself (Fig. 109). He may need, and can have, the assistance of people qualified in the various phases of ranch planning.

A plan is of prime importance to any ranching operation, but especially where management details of both the range and livestock are dependent on time of application. More mismanagement can be attributed to improperly timed adjustments than possibly any other factor. It is also important that the essentials of the plan be recorded in some fashion. It may be a detailed written plan or it may be a set of notes used as a daily reference by the rancher (Fig. 110). Regardless, those essential elements of the plan should be specific as to what will be done, when it will be done, and how it will be done. If these details are not considered and planned at the outset, it is doubtful they will be carried out to the extent of achieving the planned objectives.

Fig. 109. A range management plan must be based on logical decisions made by the rancher and his family. It is their cooperative effort that will make it work. (Jack, Dorothy, Cody, and David Douglas, Hale Center, Texas.)

Fig. 110. The Ed Harrell ranch home on the brink of Palo Dura Canyon, Armstrong County, Texas. The ranch plan for the Harrell ranch is written in detail and kept current by day-to-day pocket notebook decisions.

APPRAISING SOIL, WATER, AND PLANT RESOURCES

Although the ranch operator may have a good idea of what he has by way of soil, water, and plant resources, he may never have looked at them in terms of their needs or their potential. Too often these resources are accepted as "good soil or poor soil; deep soil or shallow soil; plenty of grass or out of grass"; "we had good rains"; or, "it's awfully dry." These make for good conversation but have little value insofar as the real resources of the range are concerned.

In order to plan for good management and highest production from the range, there are certain basic facts that must be known and taken into account. For a grazing unit or pasture, and ultimately for the entire ranch, the kinds of land, or the various range sites, must be known for what they will produce. They are basic to the entire ranching operation. The kind of plants growing on each site and the kind that are potential to the site are basic planning objectives (Fig. 111). How various soils respond to available rainfall, and areas where run-in affects production are important factors to planning. Areas with limited production should be recognized for what they are, if nothing more than a watershed for more productive lands (Fig. 112).

These and many other details of the range are "written on the landscape" if only they are looked for and evaluated. It is these facts, along with livestock and other managerial factors, that serve to identify the problems of range and ranch management.

IDENTIFYING THE PROBLEMS

Identifying the problems of the range, management of the livestock, and operation of the ranch in general are the most important steps in planning for efficiency of a sustained enterprise. The rancher must realize that he has problems, know what they are, and find out how they affect his operations and income. Before he has a basis for sound decisions in planning, he must also know that it is important to do something about them. Furthermore, he must know practical solutions to his problems and sincerely want to do something about them if progress is to be made.

Basic problems and range practices should not be confused. Although the application of certain range practices may seem to be a problem at times, this is not the real problem. The real problems that

Fig. 111. A desert range with near potential production. Chino grama and black grama are in good amounts, with numerous desert shrubs that are climax to the site.

Fig. 112. A desert range producing little if any desirable forage. Though this range serves primarily as a watershed, most of the water goes down the creek, whereas it should be conserved and spread over more productive sites.

need to be identified have to do primarily with the existing conditions of the range vegetation. Is the kind of vegetation that exists the kind that should be there and the kind the rancher wants (Fig. 113)? Does the vegetation need to be changed to improve the composition? What will be required to make such a change? Is it merely to improve what is there or will something have to be removed and replaced by something better? Is there a brush problem, requiring brush removal and control before range improvement is possible (Fig. 114)? Is range seeding necessary before a sustained production of high quality range forage is possible (Fig. 115)? Is uniform use by good distribution of grazing being made of the range? Is there an erosion problem on the range (Fig. 116)? Are there water control measures needed to make effective use of rainfall? Are there adequate facilities for handling and managing livestock, the tool for getting range management applied?

These and perhaps other questions pertinent to the range resource are the basis for a range improvement and range management plan. Such a plan would not only involve needs of the range but logically must conform to the needs for livestock management and sound ranch operations.

Seldom is it possible for a ranch plan to fit a prescribed pattern of treatment and management. And certainly no two situations would be alike. Therefore it is always necessary to tailor the plan to fit the individual situation. That is why it is the rancher himself who can develop the details of a plan that will provide the requirements of solutions to existing problems.

Aside from the problems of the range there are also those related to the care and management of the livestock. It is not enough to plan only for the benefit of the range. The produce from the range is marketed through livestock. Therefore, any management plan that does not take into account the needs for efficient livestock production is not a sound plan for that operation.

Seasonal use and sometimes concentrated use of a range may be beneficial to the range but may not provide an adequate diet for the livestock. A change in the kind of livestock may be a solution. Improperly spaced water locations may be detrimental to both the range and the livestock. Improving the water situation may be beneficial to both the range and the livestock. On the other hand, an over-watered range may actually contribute to overgrazing and range deterioration. A grazing management system may be ideal for the

Fig. 113. A good range of blue and sideoats grama, with yucca invasion the problem. Yucca control and improved health, vigor, and production of the grass would be the planned treatment.

Fig. 114. This range should be open grassland. Brush control and improvement of the sparse stand of weakened grass plants will be needed as a solution to the problems indicated here. (Photo courtesy U.S. Soil Conservation Service, Texas.)

Fig. 115. This stand of creosotebush is all this range will support. To change to a grass range will require brush control and range seeding.

Fig. 116. Water control measures will be necessary to prevent this gully from eventually destroying several acres of the most productive land on this ranch. (Photo courtesy U.S. Soil Conservation Service, Texas.)

range but unworkable for efficient livestock management in keeping classes or kinds separated or in a logical breeding program. Some ranchers are opposed to shifting stock from one pasture to another to effect a sound grazing management plan. An alternate plan might be to simply adjust the stocking rate to insure no more than proper use of the range on a yearlong basis.

Livestock needs must be provided in a sound range management plan. Usually, without a plan, these needs are given primary consideration over needs of the range. Range improvement can only result in more and better feed for the livestock, therefore contributing materially to livestock needs and production.

ALTERNATIVES AND FLEXIBILITY IN PLANNING

There is no enterprise more dynamic than a ranching operation. It is a production based on natural resources of the land and natural instincts of foraging animals. Neither of these factors are entirely predictable, and only through manipulation of the livestock can the rancher have any control of either production or management of the range. Even then, such control is effective only to the extent that it is correlated with the factors of plant development and plant reactions.

Because of these uncertainties, it is important that there be alternatives of treatment and flexibility, especially in management, if a practical and effective plan is to be developed and carried out.

Alternatives of treatment are nothing more than the various ways of achieving a common objective. To illustrate, if the existing vegetation needs to be improved to strengthen the stand and increase production, it may be done either by adjusting numbers to the proper grazing capacity or by a deferred grazing program. Proper use and improved production could be achieved by either system. If the composition of the vegetation is the problem, it may be changed by range seeding, if the site will permit, or it may be changed by properly using the range. The latter will take longer but cost less in cash outlay. There may be a brush problem that could be approached either by mechanically removing the brush or by the use of chemicals. These factual examples point up the fact that although range problems may be many and varied, seldom is there but a single approach to solving any of them.

Also, inasmuch as the ranching operation is at the mercies of the environment, particularly climate, the entire operation must be flexible enough to cope with the weather. The best management plan can go awry by an abnormality in the rainfall pattern. Unexpected economic conditions may also dictate a change from an orderly, planned marketing program. There may be unavoidable disruptions in planned rangeland treatment programs, such as brush control or range seeding. These and many other unforeseen occurrences may arise to disrupt a smoothly operating management plan.

Realizing that such happenings are inevitable, any plan for the operation and management of a ranch should provide for safeguards against such events. In the interest of good range management with flexibility, the most important basic principle is a reserve feed supply. It may be in the form of stored feed, or perhaps it is more conducive to good range management if it is unused forage over the range. A system of management with a reserve pasture or two is a good plan. Grazing use that insures at least 50 per cent of the last production being left at the end of the grazing season is a cushion for emergency use. Although not to the best interest of the grass, such use in an emergency is not too detrimental provided subsequent management insures recovery.

Perhaps the greatest assurance of flexibility in any management plan is always maintaining a percentage of the grazing load as a readily marketable class of stock. A rancher in the cow-calf business is wise to devote a portion of his range to stocker cattle. Likewise, mutton sheep or goats can be profitable while they too provide built-in flexibility in the ranching operation.

In almost any grazing management plan, even slight adjustments are desirable to make the treatment more effective. Such adjustments are quite common in the application of practices of management relative to the principles of seasonal use, distribution of grazing, and kinds of livestock. However, they most often occur in relation to proper grazing use of the range. It is only logical to expect such needed adjustments due to the expected wide deviations from normal rainfall in much of the range country. It is not uncommon for these deviations to occur within a single season, making sometimes drastic adjustments necessary. The good rancher places about as much emphasis on that part of his planning to provide alternatives of treatment and flexibility as he does on the management plan itself. When this is done, he seldom gets into serious trouble in his operations.

PROBLEM ANALYSIS IN RANGE MANAGEMENT PLANNING

Even though the problems encountered in the development of a range management and range improvement program may be varied to encompass the entire ranching operation, the primary objective is to produce more and better range forage. This can be done by adhering to the basic principles involved in the establishment, growth, and production of range forage plants.

The individual grazing unit or pasture is the most practical entity for various problems involved. At least it is the unit of management that can be used in both the analysis and solution to range problems. But within that unit there will be few too many individual vegetation characteristics that can be measured, evaluated, planned, and treated for improvement and use. These may include individual plant species, plant associations, range sites, soil-plant or soil-plant-air-water relationships. Primarily, the problems that can be most readily identified include: (1) those having to do with changes that have occurred in the plant composition, such as invasion of low-grade and undesirable plants; poor distribution of grazing use; water facilities and other livestock control and management improvements improperly located; less than adequate use of all forage plants, indicating the wrong kind of livestock; soil erosion and water losses from uncontrolled run-off; low plant vigor of the better forage plants; and heavy use of current forage production. One or any combination of these forage production problems must be analyzed as to what they are, where they occur and, most important, why they exist. Without such an analysis there is no logical starting place for a management plan.

Although the grazing unit or pasture must be planned for treatment and use in its entirety, the various components, namely, range sites, must be considered individually (Figs. 117 and 118). They become the criteria on which planned treatment and use is based for the grazing unit. The various problem indicators enumerated above must be reconciled with the general characteristics of each site. These characteristics and related problems, and particularly preference use, indicate the relative importance of the site to the grazing unit. Such an analysis of each individual site classifies it in regard to its relative importance in management of the grazing unit. Such a classification indicates the range site(s) that require first priority as to planned treatment and use. Of course, other sites within the unit are not to

Fig. 117. Where two or more distinct range sites occur as above—a deep valley site and a rocky hill site—each must be analyzed separately and the need of each incorporated into the management plan.

Fig. 118. When a pasture is uniform as to range sites and vegetation, both problems and solutions are simplified in a grazing management plan.

be minimized or disregarded in the treatment and use plan. Their treatment and use will be satisfactory when that of the better, or key, sites have been properly planned and carried out.

It is important that this procedure be followed for each grazing unit or pasture of the entire ranch. To be sure that the plan is all-inclusive and adequate, some sort of record should be kept as the analysis is made for each unit. This is necessary regardless of whether the job is being done by a trained technician, a consultant, or the rancher himself. Small details are easily overlooked, but often are very significant to the right plan.

Specific plans, either as to treatment or use, should not be made for the individual grazing unit at the time of problem analysis. To do so almost invariably results in loss of time, inadequate planning, and often a state of confusion in trying to make such a plan fit the overall ranch. The most logical procedure is to identify the problems and needs of each grazing unit of the ranch, then start the planning process, taking into account each grazing unit involved.

RANGE IMPROVEMENT NEEDS AND MANAGEMENT NEEDS

Time spent in thoroughly analyzing each grazing unit or pasture will usually result in an ultimate saving of time and a better planning job. Such an analysis affords the opportunity to determine the needs of important plants, range improvement needs, and appropriate range management for that grazing unit. Not only are the more or less specific needs identified, but clues and possibilities of how they can be met will begin to unfold as these analyses progress from one grazing unit to another over the ranch. Keeping notes on these possibilities as observations are made and conclusions reached is also a helpful step in the final planning procedure.

After each grazing unit on the ranch has been examined and analyzed, firsthand information is available regarding the range forage resource, range improvement needs, and management needs for the entire ranch. But the fact that it is available by individual grazing units, and not as an overall for the entire ranch, signifies the needed flexibility for practical combinations of treatment and management plans.

Procedures for gathering this type information have evolved and been developed over many years. Some have been of a rather exact nature while others have been more generalized. Technical agencies have had the lead in these developments, and continue to improve on them through use and research. Such procedures have been of varying degrees of intensity and have been identified somewhat according to procedures involved. Generally, they have been known as range surveys, range inventories, range site and condition classification, and, when of least intensity, just a record of key plants for management. Information from these procedures has been recorded, primarily by technical people to whom much credit is due. However, as a tool for use in managing a range or ranch, unless the rancher or range manager actively participates in the development of such information, it is of little value to him. The shrewd technician will be sure that the rancher understands what has been recorded, or will otherwise furnish him an understandable interpretation that will permit a practical application of the findings.

To date, the range site and condition type of inventory has proved quite appropriate for rancher use, provided he is conversant with the simple principles involved. These he can usually grasp readily with a minimum of explanation, as they are depicted on the range. It is encouraging that many ranchers are becoming quite proficient in recognizing the vegetation on their range, its condition, and its needs, and what should be planned by way of treatment and management.

Regardless of the procedure used in evaluating each grazing unit, once this job is done it is a basis for knowing the overall condition of the vegetation of the ranch as well as improvement and management needs. With this information at hand, the planning procedure may logically begin. Properly analyzed and interpreted, such information is all that is needed by one trained and experienced in the field of range management. In brief, it should enable the qualified range technician to be completely abreast with the rancher who has known his ranch for twenty-five years, at least as to the resources at hand.

CORRELATING RANGE FORAGE RESOURCES AND LIVESTOCK NUMBERS

Armed with information about the vegetation of the ranch, as described above, a plan of treatment and management can be developed to achieve the desired objectives. Such a plan, however, can be applied only by the management and manipulation of the livestock, which are the tools of range management.

The next step is to determine the grazing value of the entire range in its present condition. This determination should never be a cold-blooded "acres per cow" or "cows per section" conclusion, as is all too frequently the procedure used. There are too many variables in the resources of a range to permit the establishment of a pinpoint grazing capacity. This, in turn, signifies seasonal adjustments and livestock manipulation if the most is to be gotten from the best possible grazing management. The smaller the operation and the smaller the grazing units, the more intensive can be the plan of management. Timely movement of livestock can be easily done, whereas on larger ranches management is more extensive and movement of livestock more difficult. This must be taken into account for a management plan to be practical. However, irrespective of the ranching setup, treatment and management needs should not be sacrificed for mere ease of handling livestock. To do so invariably defeats the purpose and objectives of such a plan.

Seldom does the age old method of stocking a pasture on the basis of so many acres per animal result in good uniform use of the entire pasture. Generally, variations in range sites and their respective quantity and quality of forage production does not induce uniform use of all sites in a pasture. Therefore, some sites will be overused while others are underused. Generally, use is limited to seasonal choice, which may or may not result in proper use of those sites.

Because of the many variations in the way ranges are grazed free choice, livestock preferences need to be taken into account if maximum production and uniform proper use are to result. Such variations include plant reactions to seasonal development, seasonal palatability, accessibility, distribution of grazing, the kind of livestock suited to the range, and possibly other factors that can affect the grazing value of the range. Full value should be given each grazing unit without imposing improper grazing use on any part of it.

An evaluation of the grazing value of each grazing unit is a reliable index to the grazing capacity of the ranch. But to summarize these values and set forth an absolute grazing capacity figure is usually a misleading interpretation. Depending on how livestock will graze, it may be high or it may be low even under the best management plan that can be devised. The several natural variations listed above may, individually or in combination, have a material influence on grazing values of individual grazing units over a period of time.

Seasonal palatability of desirable forage plants is perhaps the vegetative characteristic most often misleading as regards the grazing value of a pasture. From the standpoint of acreage, an extensive site within a pasture may support a dominant species of grass that is palatable for only a short season of the year. Tobosa grass, on many ranges of the southwest, is an example of such a grass. A year-long stocking rate established at the time this grass is palatable, usually at the beginning of the spring growing season, would very likely be erroneous. At that time, any rate set to use available forage would be much too high when palatability and nutritive quality of the grass decline. Here, seasonal adjustment in stocking rates are necessary in a sound management plan. There are many instances throughout the range country where a normal stocking rate would seriously overuse the forage of an important range site during a short period of high palatability. Wherever these situations occur, seasonal adjustments in stocking rates to fit the particular condition are in order.

These are the kinds of situations that need to be recognized and taken into account in determining the true grazing value of the entire range. It may not be easy, or in some instances it may not even be possible, to include in a plan all the various needed adjustments in grazing use of the range. But it is important to know what they are and where they are in consideration of alternatives and flexibility of the grazing plan.

Next in importance to a reasonably accurate inventory of the grazing resource of a range is a summary inventory of the livestock, including game animals, that graze the range. Usually the livestock inventory must be summarized on two separate bases, depending on the kind and numbers that have been using the range, and on an interpretation of the vegetation inventory into animal grazing values. Although at the outset the kind of livestock may not be of first importance in this latter interpretation, this becomes an important factor in the final planning, in order that the kind best suited to the range or even segments of the range be recognized.

The important concern in this phase of management planning is establishing a reasonable balance between range forage production and the livestock and game animals that will be used to harvest that forage. Perhaps the greatest problem in range management is that of preventing overuse of the range. Generally, overuse is a result of too many livestock grazing the range. However, the right seasonal adjustments, along with proper distribution of grazing use of all the range, very often can be compensating factors. They will be brought to light when the proper inventory analysis of the range vegetation has been made.

These determinations should be made before any conclusion is drawn about the proper balance between forage production and live-stock inventories. Based on close grazing around water locations, or because of overuse of small trap pastures, or even because of overuse of certain key sites within a pasture, it is easy to assume there is too much livestock. However, such a snap judgment is dangerous. It may be correct, but it should not be considered so until the entire range has been given at least a preliminary examination, and then only when there is conclusive evidence as to how the entire range has been used and how the vegetation has reacted to that use. Facts that are well-founded and substantiated by production and other records from the operation make the planning process essentially a set of natural conclusions as to needs and possibilities.

From there on, the planning procedure is merely that of determining what will be done, where it will be done, when it will be done, and how it will be done. This, of course, may entail some complicated techniques. However, with needs of the range recognized, and with the knowledge, experience, and skill of the rancher in managing and operating the ranch, a logical plan can always be worked out. Experience in ranch planning bears out the fact that even the most difficult of situations will unfold like Queen Elizabeth's fan, once a beginning point has evolved. Such a point will usually be recognized as a plan of treatment and management for a single significant grazing unit or pasture. Usually all others will fall into place around that first unit.

In ranch planning to determine treatment and management needs, it is always desirable to include the entire ranch at the outset. This is not always possible, and when it cannot be done it is well to consider a segment of the ranch, preferably of two or more pastures, and initiate a suitable plan. When this is necessary, the initial plan itself should specify when and where the planning process will be continued over the remainder of the ranch. This is a determination for the rancher to make, with, of course, any assistance that is available to him. In any event, that continued planning should be adhered to with as much concern as in the original planning.

IMPORTANT CONSIDERATIONS IN RANCH PLANNING

Planning for the treatment, management, and best use of rangeland is interesting and rewarding. It requires knowledge and skill along with horse sense and good judgment. Without this latter attribute, no amount of knowledge, training, or improvised skill can be exerted to develop a plan that will meet the conservation and management needs and at the same time be practical. Without these characteristics a plan is really not a plan, at least not a plan that will be followed to a productive conclusion.

Although rewarding, results from effort put forth in ranch planning are not immediately forthcoming. In fact, results may be so slow that progressive achievement is scarcely noticeable. But one may be assured that with patience, perseverance, and time, there will be rewarding results from a well-developed and properly carried out ranch plan. Even during that time indicators of a trend toward progressive improvement will make themselves known. Within themselves, they are sufficiently rewarding to claim the interest of the planner, whether he be a technician or the rancher. In time, progressive achievements will blossom forth in what might be termed a transformation of resources from the point of beginning.

Ranch planning is never done in exactly the same manner by any two individuals. Each will have his own approach, techniques, and points of emphasis, all of which can achieve the same objective. Because of these human differences, no one person can tell, teach, or train another in the exact details of ranch planning. Neither is this necessary. However, certain principles of ranch planning should be recognized by all who become involved in this field of endeavor. Some of the more important ones are as follows:

1. Become reasonably familiar with the entire ranch operation before attempting to draw conclusions or to make planning decisions.

2. Find and identify range indicators as to range trends and range condition.

3. Deal with one grazing unit or pasture at a time. Identify treatment and management needs as they are encountered. Make a record of these findings.

4. In making vegetation inventories and analyses, don't misjudge current range use for range conditions. Both overuse and underuse can be misleading.

5. Don't plan anything that is not important to that ranching operation. If it is planned, be sure everyone concerned understands and agrees to that plan.

6. Be sure the plan is specific regarding an adequate balance between available forage and livestock numbers. If anything, tip the balance in favor of available forage and feed reserves.

7. Don't activate the plan on the most seriously depleted pasture of any on the ranch. Start on a better-condition pasture that will respond more quickly. Thus, the total feed supply will be on the increase, which will benefit the operation. The poor pasture will respond more slowly, and in fact may continue to decline for a year or so before improvement will be noted. This usually results in more pressure on the better pastures and further deterioration of them.

8. Provide for a feed reserve for drought years. Such a reserve may include one or more reserve pastures; a supply of supplemental feed as hay, silage, or even a concentrate; supplemental pasture, if cropland is available; and that reserve that remains by properly using the range; that is, by always leaving 50 per cent by weight of the current or last forage production. Rather than being a part of the management plan, this reserve forage should be available for emergency use. Recovery from emergency use of a properly used range is not too difficult, provided extra measures of management are used to compensate for the abuse it may have had.

9. Keep the ranch plan simple, workable, and practical. Don't let it be cluttered with extraneous material. If such material is available and worth something to the ranch operator, he needs it, but not as a part of his ranch plan.

10. Keep the plan active. Let it be a working guide for day to day ranching operations. It should be basic to efficiency in production of the most important crop in American agriculture, grass.

Chapter 14

LIVESTOCK, THE TOOL IN RANGE MANAGEMENT

Livestock control and management, the rancher's tool for achieving range management. Range adaptations of kinds and classes of livestock, the criteria for range management. Soil and topographic influences on range forage and livestock grazing. Grazing value of range forage indicative of livestock management and use of the range. Influences imposed by ranch improvements regulate livestock grazing and range use. Grazing habits of livestock and their effects on grazing use and management of rangelands.

Livestock and ranch improvements are the only tools the rancher has for carrying out a range management program. These, along with good judgment and a knowledge of both livestock and grass, are essential to a profitable and successful ranching operation.

Different areas of the western ranching country have characteristics that distinguish one from another. These characteristics are primarily those having to do with topography, soil, climate, and the resulting kind of range forage that can be produced. Regardless of these characteristics, the basic principles of plant management and of livestock management are essentially the same in any area.

Because of such variations, recognized range management techniques must be adopted according to each kind of country to obtain productive use and yet maintain the range. Few instances and situations are encountered where this is not possible and practical.

RANGE ADAPTATIONS BY KINDS AND CLASSES OF LIVESTOCK

In a general way, kinds and classes of livestock are adapted to the kind of range country that best meets their production needs. These areas have been recognized and designated on the premise of two significant concepts: the suitability of the country, and the native ability and experience of ranchmen. Historically, these factors have largely identified an area with the production of kinds and classes of livestock.

Certain areas are specifically adapted to certain kinds of livestock. For example, the Edwards Plateau of west central Texas is sheep and goat country. This area is further divided with goats more suitably adapted to the southern, more rugged portion. Montana, Idaho, and other mountainous states are well suited to sheep production. These states, as well as Arizona, Utah, and portions of others are recognized for their value as sheep ranges due to seasonal variations. Valleys and desert ranges are highly suitable for winter range, and the adjacent mountains provide excellent summer range.

The Great Plains states are especially well suited to cattle production because of the forage resources, topographic features, and climate to which cattle are well suited. To the east, where rainfall is abundant, kinds of livestock other than sheep and goats are best suited. This is due to parasites and diseases that seem to be associated with more humid conditions and which are limiting factors in the production of the smaller kinds of livestock. Furthermore, areas with high humidity, intense heat, insects, and parasites of many kinds are especially well suited to breeds of cattle with built-in resistance to these conditions. The Brahman breed, with its various crosses and hybrid developments, is especially well suited to this type of country (Fig. 119). Their ability to perspire over the body rather than in the restricted area of the nose aids in withstanding intense heat and humidity. Also, their thick, tough, and flexible hide is more resistant to bloodsucking insects than that of European breeds. Their rugged vigor insures greater resistance to parasites than other breeds.

Over much of the range country there will be overlapping as to kinds of livestock in almost every different natural environment. And these instances are not without success, owing largely to the rancher's ability to satisfactorily manage both his livestock and his range forage resource, for the livestock of his choice. The once prevalent concept that various kinds of livestock could not make compatible use of the same range has proved erroneous both through research and rancher experience. But good livestock management is necessary if the range is not abusively grazed.

A serious misjudgment in the management of some ranges has been due to the wrong concept of what various kinds of animals will

Fig. 119. Brahman cattle, with their characteristics of perspiring over the body, thick hide, and rugged vigor, are well-adapted to a hot, humid climate. (Photo courtesy U.S. Soil Conservation Service, Louisiana.)

actually graze. Ranges on which the three important categories of forage plants, grasses, browse, and forbs are found are generally subjected to serious grazing abuse. Inasmuch as cattle prefer grass, sheep graze forbs, and goats have a preference for browse, all three categories of plants will be grazed if the three kinds of livestock are run. Too often the range is stocked to near capacity with cattle as the main enterprise. A number of sheep are added to use the forbs, and then a few goats to use the browse.

The fallacy of this judgment in grazing management is not in the mixing of kinds of livestock but in the actual grazing pattern each will follow. Although sheep have a strong preference for forbs when they are in a palatable state and goats and deer like browse, they all have a degree of preference for grass. Cattle are primarily grass eaters, but they too like to mix their diet by taking some browse and some forbs. It is these overlapping selections, even during the lush grazing period, that often results in abusive grazing use of perhaps all categories of forage on the range when stocked with mixed kinds of livestock. This condition will be further aggravated as individual plant species in various categories reach maturity and become unpalatable.

Because of these facts, it is important for the range and livestock manager to have knowledge of the grazing habits of his animals, as well as a knowledge of what is available on his range and when it is grazable by choice.

THE INFLUENCE OF SOIL AND TOPOGRAPHY ON HOW LIVESTOCK GRAZE

Soil and topography have a strong influence on the kind of vegetation that will grow on that particular spot of ground. In fact, the soil itself is basic to the kinds of plants that will grow (Figs. 120 and 121). This, when coupled with the influence of slope, exposure, elevation, and very often the depth and maturity of the soil, largely regulates the kinds of plants within a given climate. Not only do these factors influence the kinds of plants, but they strongly influence the quality and nutritive value of plants. This, in turn, has a strong influence as to the kinds of livestock that will best use areas that are characterized by various soil and topographic conditions.

Domestic livestock are well equipped with instinct, energy, and a will to satisfy their needs. These are the driving forces that cause them to choose the range they use. Instinctively some kinds of livestock, namely, the horse and to a degree the ancestral development of domestic cattle, prefer more level to rolling terrain because such were the conditions from which they came. In contrast, the goat, and to a lesser degree the sheep, originated in more rugged terrain where steep slopes, and rough, rocky topography was their habitat. Thus it is natural that these various kinds of livestock continue to thrive in areas more comparable to their native habitat, which is today a logical interpretation of their adaptability.

This is not to say that any kind of livestock will completely confine their grazing use to a favored kind of country. It is well-known that all kinds of livestock and game animals will use all kinds of range land, but not always by preference or even most efficiently as to either the livestock or the range.

Because of these preferences in grazing, there has, perhaps, been more range deterioration brought about than for any other one reason, especially in mountainous areas. The usual custom is to stock a

Fig. 120. Sandy soil naturally produces tall grasses, usually in abundance. It is therefore best suited to cattle. Also, cattle can maneuver over sand better than can sheep and goats.

Fig. 121. Shallow, rocky soils often produce dense stands of brush species that provide excellent browse for goats. But goats also like forage other than browse. (Photo courtesy U.S. Soil Conservation Service, Texas.)

range on the basis of so many animal units to the section or the pasture. In most instances, these stocking rates are within reason as to the amount of forage produced on that acreage to meet livestock needs. The question is, does each animal harvest all his allotted acreage uniformly? The answer is, usually not, with topography being among the most significant obstacles. Mountain ranges always have steep and often high and rocky slopes. At the base are valleys and often low, rolling talus slopes that are accessible and easily grazed (Fig. 122). The latter areas will be grazed and overgrazed by horses, cattle, sheep, and goats in this order of preference grazing. Generally, this will be range deterioration to the first degree when cattle and horses use the range; to a lesser degree with sheep; and possibly not severely by goats. Goats instinctively prefer the rougher mountainous terrain as well as the forage often available on the higher elevations.

When this type of management is practiced it simply adds up to the fact that, although stocked on a reasonable acreage basis, the animals spend too much time on too small a portion of the range (Fig. 123).

When these grazing use patterns may logically be expected, the solution to more efficient use of all the forage resource is a somewhat more intensive grazing management program. Such a program may include one or a combination of several practical techniques of management. They would include: (1) stocking on the basis of the favored areas of grazing, with added numbers at the season and for the period the steep slopes would be taken by choice; (2) the use of mixed kinds of livestock including those that would graze both kinds of range by preference as cattle and goats; (3) a deferred system of grazing that would insure a rest period for the more favored grazing area during the critical growth period (spring or fall and switch in alternate years); (4) a deferred rotation system of grazing; and (5) fencing out areas according to grazing preference.

Where topography and inaccessibility strongly influence the grazing pattern, the most difficult range management problem is proper distribution of grazing. Achieving this basic principle of range management requires not only knowledge of both range forage and livestock requirements but practical ways and means of carrying out the solution.

Fig. 122. Cattle will use the valley and low, smooth hills in the fore-ground rather uniformly. The high, steep mountains in back are best used by goats, sheep, and game animals.

Fig. 123. Although this is primarily a cattle range, 75 per cent of the use is in narrow valleys and lower slopes of the steep lands. Thus, these areas are usually overused while the steeper slopes are used very lightly.

NUTRITIONAL QUALITY AND PALATABILITY OF RANGE PLANTS AFFECT GRAZING

Among the numerous factors that influence the way livestock, including game animals, graze a range, none is more significant than the nutritive quality and palatability of the forage. This characteristic of the forage may vary widely with different kinds of plants, specific groups of plants, or even individual plants, but with equal importance to management of the range. In like manner, climatic and seasonal variations in palatability and nutritive quality of plants or groups of plants will strongly influence grazing management.

By instinct, grazing animals know what plants, on which site, and when they have the highest grazing value, both as to palatability and nutritional qualities. Hence, animals will change their pattern of grazing to conform to changes in the grazing qualities of plants. More than any other factor, these qualities determine where, for how long, and the degree of use that will be made of range forage. This, in turn, largely determines the grazing distribution of the range, which is a cardinal principle of range management.

Throughout the range country are examples of livestock grazing preferences that directly affect management of the range. No doubt the most universal example of range forage selectivity is the indiscriminate use of the tender and succulent growth of almost anything green in early spring. As a tool in range management, grazing otherwise low-quality forage in early spring is a good practice. To do so results in increased production from the range and removes the forage from competition with other more desirable plants, usually perennials that will grow on the site.

Other examples of selective use owing to plants having characteristics that affect animal choices are: the use of coarse stemmed grasses in early stages of growth before they become woody, unpalatable, and low in food value; (2) in the southwest, the selection of buffalograss over curley mesquitegrass when growing together, because of the palatability and often nutritive quality of one over the other; (3) the use of cool season grasses in fall and early spring when they are more palatable and nutritious than at any other time of the year; and (4) species that are minor over the range as a whole, but abundant on certain selected sites. For example, puffsheath dropseed (*Sporobolus neglectus*) and poverty dropseed (*Sporobolus vaginiflorus*), are both well adapted to rather poor, shallow sites. In early October, and at no other time, these grasses become very palatable, especially to horses and to a lesser degree to cattle.

In practically all range areas are plants that have a high degree, and sometimes unique, selectivity by grazing animals. Sometimes the incidence may be minor and insignificant, but even so they provide definite clues and often dictate the best management for the range.

As previously discussed, an important and often abundant range forage is the various threeawn species of the genus *Aristida*. On many ranges, one or more of these species make up more than half the range forage available. Because these species, for the most part, green up a little earlier in the spring than other warm season grasses, they are a preferred grass.

When threeawn is abundant on a range that is stocked, even at no more than a proper rate for the total forage production, if seasonal selectivity is not taken into account, a downward trend in range condition will likely result. This is due not to heavy use of the threeawn but to subsequent overuse of other grasses plus the inevitable deferment and regrowth of the threeawn and its competitive ability over other grasses. Such a trend is never stopped or reversed without a change in the control and management of the livestock. What would be the logical livestock and range management to alleviate such a downward trend of the range? The solution to such a problem is to watch the grazing animals. When they start selectively grazing those less-desirable plants, threeawn in this case, stock the range with as many head or animal units that the threeawn will support; encourage them to use it as heavily as they will. By continuing to observe the grazing of the range, when these less-desirable plants are being left ungrazed and other more-desirable plants are selected, adjust the grazing load to what those better plants will support. The management plan should have provided a place for these animals to permit this adjustment.

Granted that this amount of manipulation of livestock would be objectionable to some ranchers, but range management is no longer a matter of precedent, convenience, or "leave it to the cow" type of operation. It requires interest, skill, knowledge, and, in a sense, intensification of the operation. The manipulation of livestock is no longer the "unpardonable sin of the range" it once was. Livestock, even on large ranches, are becoming more and more domesticated and subject to treatment, handling, and management. More intensive use of them as a tool in range management is today no more of a restriction and limitation on their foraging habits than was the innovation of the barbwire fence.

TRAVEL DISTANCE INFLUENCES LIVESTOCK GRAZING

The distance from water to a favored site for grazing will influence the use of the range. Animals will not only overuse a site near the water location but will utilize less desirable kinds of plants rather than walk excessive distances to better feed. Because of this, the range near the water location or any point of concentration will be used more heavily than sites farther removed (Figs. 124 and 125). This becomes a factor in management that will, if not adequately accounted for, become progressively extended as these areas inevitably become larger. Because of this, the degree of use around a point of concentration can never be used as the key site in judging the condition or current degree of use of a range.

GRAZING HABITS OF LIVESTOCK

Livestock have natural grazing habits as well as those they acquire as a result of their environment. As insignificant as habits may seem, if they are not taken into account in the management plan, they can have serious effects on the range.

Various kinds of animals have different social orders in relation to each other. Also their social orders may vary with the season of the year or even because of imposed management and facilities. Cattle have a natural tendency to disperse over the range in small groups, especially mature animals (Fig. 126). Young cattle are more inclined to remain in larger herds but gradually acquire greater dispersion as they increase in age and become more self reliant in their grazing pattern (Fig. 127). Horses have a tendency to stay together, even in large bands, particularly stock horses. They, more than any other kind of livestock, damage the range by physical destruction of grass in their grazing and watering habits. Because of their ability to travel, they will range farther from water than will other kinds of range animals. From these more distant areas, when watering time comes, the band will usually travel the distance in a lope or run. They usually establish and follow trails or travelways that are used both

Fig. 124. Depleted condition around water location of a blue and black grama range. Note the bare ground, deep trails, and invasion of mesquite. The mesquite extends a half-mile from the well. At ¾ mile, normal conditions for that range were in evidence. Water locations are 2 to 3 miles apart.

Fig. 125. Although closely grazed, this sandy land range has not deteriorated in condition. Timely deferments allow areas around water to recover from normal concentration and use.

Fig. 126. Mature cattle, especially when calves are small, prefer to graze in small groups.

Fig. 127. Young cattle tend to stay in large groups, even when not restricted with fences. This herd of steer yearlings is trailing to water.

going to and returning from water. The forage in and along these travelways is subjected to severe abuse from repeated pounding by hoofs until plants can no longer survive.

All kinds of livestock have the habit of following a path of least resistance. This means travelways usually follow a natural drain or valley that is always a most productive site. Trails and adjacent bare areas occur permitting, first, moderate water run-off and soil removal (Fig. 128). With time, this becomes more serious until in many instances whole valleys may be destroyed for forage production (Fig. 129).

In contrast to cattle and horses, sheep and goats are more inclined to graze together in bands. This, no doubt, can be attributed largely to the earlier methods of handling these kinds of livestock. In early day ranching, herding of sheep and goats in large bands was the most logical method of control and management. With improved ranching operations, where private lands are involved and to some extent on public lands, fencing and other ranch improvement facilities have replaced herding. These developments have brought about changes in normal grazing patterns. Animals have become more independent in their choice, both as to areas and plants they use, as well as to their grazing and watering habits. These developments have definite advantages but are not without disadvantages that need to be taken into account for good range management.

When sheep and goats are given free access to a range, they become habitual in grazing patterns of the range. That is, they select a part of the range that meets their immediate needs and desires as to quantity and quality of feed that is accessible to water. Sheep in particular will sometimes confine their grazing to a rather restricted area as long as they can satisfy their food requirements reasonably well. To do so usually results in overuse of some if not all of the better forage plants of that area. Such use of these more favored areas throughout a pasture is usually in contrast to other sites within that pasture that may actually be underused. To continually stock a pasture on this basis year long, and possibly for a period of years, usually precludes the advantage of natural seasonal use of certain forage plants throughout the pasture.

This type of habitual site preference to grazing by any kind of livestock, but especially by sheep, with their close grazing ability, usually results in decreased production from both the range and the livestock. Usually two of the cardinal principles of range manage-

Fig. 128. Stock trails too often are the beginning of severe erosion. (Photo courtesy U.S. Soil Conservation Service, Texas.)

Fig. 129. When stock trail erosion is not controlled, vast areas of productive land are destroyed. Note the wire checks installed in an effort to reclaim this eroded area. (Photo courtesy U.S. Soil Conservation Service, Texas.)

Fig. 130. Even when not herded, goats tend to stay in rather large bands. They travel to water in bands, then back to the type of country of their choice, in this case, the steep, rocky mountainside.

ment are flagrantly violated: intensity of grazing use of the better plants, and improper distribution of grazing.

In connection with this point of site selection and grazing habits, goats are not as restrictive in their choice of sites as are other kinds of livestock. They too will select the type of country best suited to their needs and use it frequently and continuously (Fig. 130). However, they also have a roving habit to satisfy a curiosity that is a part of their makeup. The late Wallace Dameron, Superintendent of Texas Ranch Experiment Station at Sonora, Texas, once said: "There is little if anything that can be done to control the grazing habits of un-herded goats; they will make the whole pasture twice a day anyway." This habit alone gives credence to the goat more than any other class of livestock in the self application of proper grazing distribution in a range management program.

Another instinctive habit of livestock grazing, particularly cattle and sheep, is that of grazing into the wind. To do so evidently enhances their selection of plants they are grazing by the delicate sense of smell they possess. This, coupled with a natural instinct to graze away from a storm, sometimes puts undue pressure on a grazing unit. If the prevailing wind during a good part of the year is from the south and prevailing storms from the north, most of the grazing will be in a southerly direction. It is not uncommon to see the south side of a pasture grazed more closely and often in a lower range condition than areas to the north. This can largely be credited to the grazing habit of the livestock using the pasture, unless water location is the controlling factor.

The size and shape of a pasture, along with water locations, may have a bearing on the grazing pattern. For example, long, narrow pastures running north and south would likely be grazed repeatedly by a rather fixed pattern. Grazing would be over the same area day after day. If the water were located in the north end of the pasture, animals would graze southward and trail back to water. The same pasture with the long way running east and west would likely be grazed in a southerly direction but not necessarily over the same area each day. One day the animals might graze across the west end; the following day across the east; and even across the middle of the pasture the third day before again covering the first used west end.

Admittedly these are minor factors in range management, but they are worthy of consideration as to size, location, and direction of a pasture layout, and they become especially important in water locations when there is a choice.

Another important livestock consideration in range management is the length of time and the area that must be covered for animals to meet their body requirements for feed. For grazing animals to do well, they should be able to get their fill of nutritious forage in a two- to three-hour grazing period. This should permit them to then lie down and rest, ruminate, and have complete relaxation for complete digestion and assimilation of the food they have eaten (Fig. 131). Under ideal conditions, four or five of these graze and rest periods, with time out for water as needed, should occur during a 24-hour period. Under these circumstances, nothing short of disease or mishap can prevent the animal from being productive.

On the other hand, when conditions for grazing are any less favorable, livestock production is hampered just to that degree. A few of the many common conditions that contribute to lowered production are: livestock grazing always ahead of grass production;

Fig. 131. These cattle have had their early morning fill after two or three hours of grazing from a good productive range. They are now making good productive use of what they have eaten. (Photo courtesy U.S. Soil Conservation Service, Texas.)

Fig. 132. Cattle on an inherently low-producing range must spend most of their time in search of food for body maintenance and any additional production that is possible.

ranges producing less than their capability, due to lowered range condition; a predominance of poor quality forage plants; seasonally unpalatable plants; sparse vegetation either naturally or because of range deterioration (Fig. 132); the forage resource too far from water; range plants of poor nutritive quality; and, a kind of livestock not suited to the kind of range available. There are numerous other local situations that will disrupt the most desirable use of the range for maximum livestock production. Actually, the key to efficient range and livestock management is the amount of time and energy that must be expended by the animal in gathering the number of pounds of forage required to meet his needs. A steer on good range may be able to graze 15 to 18 pounds of high-quality forage in a two-hour period at very little expenditure of energy. This could easily result in 1½ to 2 pounds of gain per day. In contrast, on another range classed in poor condition, he may be required to graze five hours, or even almost continuously, to get the same amount of feed. Because of poor quality forage, it may require 30 pounds to furnish the same food value and body requirement for production. Even though he gets the required food value from the larger amount of forage grazed, the increased energy required by longer and perhaps more rigorous grazing periods would reduce the amount of gain that could be expected. Obviously, as available nutritious forage declines according to animal needs, the potential gain declines. Ultimately, the point of mere body maintenance is reached, and with further decline the animal can no longer maintain body weight.

Because of these animal reactions to the availability of range forage, they naturally serve as an indication of the condition and production of the range. However, animal weights, or livestock production by any other unit of measure, should not be relied on as the sole clue to range management needs. When lowered livestock weights become indicative of production from the range, damage to the range has already taken place. Needed changes in management should be made immediately to prevent further deterioration. Livestock weights and rates of gain do serve well as an indicator of a range condition and range trends. Therefore, how well the livestock are doing may be used as an indicator of the soundness of the range management program.

Chapter 15

GRAZING MANAGEMENT SYSTEMS

History of grazing management systems. Some recognized systems that have evolved. Open range- or large pasture-free choice grazing use patterns. Purpose and use of deferred grazing in management. The place of rotation grazing on rangeland. Rotation-deferred grazing systems and their practical application to many and varied ranching operations. A seasonal suitability system for undependable, low-producing ranges. High-intensity-low frequency (HILF) system, a promising new innovation. The importance of a management system for efficient and productive grazing use of rangelands.

Before the western range country was settled, and even for a period following the introduction of domestic livestock, grazing management was carried out by the animals that used the range. By all standards of evaluation, this management was not too bad. By instinct, buffalo, deer, and antelope migrated seasonally in search of feed to meet their needs. By coincidence, this migration not only benefited them but under most conditions was also a benefit to the range. However, from the beginning, the more accessible and more palatable and nutritious forage was grazed the most. Such areas usually comprised valleys and swales in broken terrain and deep productive soils of smooth country. This same problem is one of the most significant in range management today.

With the introduction of domestic livestock there began the immediate problem of competition for grass and water. This resulted in concentrated grazing near available water supplies. This problem began to magnify in intensity and scope and has continued to do so as the grazing industry has progressed through the years.

With ownership of land, along with planned control of publicly managed grazing lands, grazing use of the range has become more restrictive as to the freedom of movement of livestock. This has taken away the instinctive management ability of grazing animals, and to a degree has imposed restrictions on the rancher in carrying out good range management. In fact, too little attention has been given restrictions and confinement of livestock in the management of both privately and publicly operated grazing lands. Fortunately, in recent years the science of range management and the good judgment of progressive ranchers have taken into account the grazing habits of foraging animals and the necessity for seasonal adjustments to compensate for this lack of freedom of movement in grazing management.

SOME RECOGNIZED GRAZING MANAGEMENT SYSTEMS

Range management, one of the more recent and significant phases of plant science, has created a challenge equal to and even greater than almost any other facet of agricultural production. An integral part of this challenge has been the recognition of distinct grazing management systems that will meet the needs of both the livestock and the range, and be practical and economically feasible for the ranch operator.

With the development of this phase of plant science, a number of grazing management systems are recognized as having distinct characteristics. These characteristics are significant because, by design or as a natural event, they cause a beneficial reaction of range plants that are grazed. As these systems are discussed, it should be kept in mind that there are others, all designed to fit a kind of country and the best use of the grazing resource. Also, there are variations, adaptations, and preferences of all recognized systems to meet individual or local needs.

Considering grazing management systems somewhat in order of their recognized beginning, it is appropriate to recognize first the "open range, free choice" system. It is the least demanding on the ranch operator of any system. No doubt, this fact contributes to its popularity where it is applicable, as well as in too many instances where it is not the best system of management. Such a system is practical and feasible only where grazing units are large and include a variety of kinds of country, that is, areas of range that are different as to kinds, amounts, and season of palatability and nutrition of range forage. Such areas of variation must be sufficiently large to attract grazing for an appreciable period of time. Obviously, these conditions are found only on ranches of extremely large grazing units or pastures, or on unfenced public grazing lands where livestock movement is unrestricted.

Subsequent to the open range-free choice grazing management came the yearlong restricted grazing unit varying in size and with little regard to the kind or kinds of country involved. This system of grazing was a more or less natural result of property ownership and the barbedwire fence.

With recognition of range deterioration came deferred grazing or an occasional period of rest for pastures or ranges. This was among the first steps in scientific and planned grazing management (Fig. 133). Although not readily accepted at the outset, and with reservations still being exercised, it was a good beginning. Usually some benefit to the range resulted regardless of how applied, and certainly

Fig. 133. This southern Rocky Mountain blue grama-black grama range was deferred the entire growing season. It will provide excellent grazing during the winter months.

it has provided guidelines as a basis for much more reliable criteria as to plant reaction and management needs. Essentially, the practice of deferred grazing is basic to all good grazing management systems for the greater portion of the range country.

Rotation grazing, or the systematic movement of livestock from one grazing unit to another, although beneficial to range forage is generally not considered practical for a ranching operation. It is, however, a feasible management program where small grazing units are used. Such management is generally referred to as a pasture program rather than a range operation. Although its use is limited for rangeland, it does provide beneficial forage improvement and maintenance when used under proper conditions.

Rotation-deferred systems, a combination of principles of grazing management, is proving to be a most practical and feasible program. It is especially adaptable on privately owned land that is fenced and crossfenced into grazing units or pastures. Experience has proved that a rotation-deferred grazing management system can be initiated on at least a part of most privately owned ranching operations with very little, if any, additional fencing.

Over much of the range country, various grazing systems have been modified to provide for combinations of two or more kinds of livestock. Contrary to early thinking, multiple kinds of livestock can be managed in conformity with the basic principles of the planned system, whatever it may be. The two criteria that indicate the value of using mixed kinds of livestock are: wide variations in the terrain and topography of the country; and wide differences in the kinds of produced forage that is relished by different kinds of animals. The rough mountains interspersed with valleys and plateaus of the southwest and the mixed grass and browse covered ranges throughout the west are examples of regions where combinations of livestock contribute to good grazing management.

Every recognized grazing system has merit. But of primary concern is a system that fits the ranching operation. Only then will a system be kept in use over the years. Some systems that have proved practical and effective are discussed below.

OPEN RANGE-FREE CHOICE SYSTEM

Before the white man came to America, the entire country was used and managed essentially by wild game animals. A possible de-

Fig. 134. Even on large, unrestricted ranges, grazing pressure is usually put on more-favored areas, resulting in deterioration of those sites.

viation from this natural cohabitation of plant and animal life might have been the use of fire by Indian tribes as a means of enticing game animals to, or repelling them from, favored hunting grounds.

With the beginning of the settlement of the American West, this system of management was continued essentially uninhibited until the advent of barbedwire in the 1870's.

The fundamental principle involved in this system of management lies in the fact that grazing animals are permitted to move about over the range, restricted only by the availability of water. Consequently, they moved, free will, from one locality to another as the palatability and quality of range forage changed. These changes were generally influenced by climatic seasons. However, this was not always true, as some forage plants, including certain species of grass, declined in preference very rapidly due to maturity, coarseness, palatability or nutritive quality, within a single season.

Quality of forage is not the only factor that influences where and what animals will graze. Easily accessible grazing is always used first rather than that on steep, rough, and rocky country. Distance from water, extremes in temperatures, direction of prevailing winds, and other factors that influence grazing habits of livestock, are today recognized influences in controlling where and what animals graze.

In fact, livestock preferences will cause not only overgrazing of the most-desirable forage but can result in beneficial use of poor quality plants. This, of course, will take place only when those plants are palatable and generally when they are readily available.

These habits and preferences of grazing invariably lead to the more-favorable areas being grazed first and the most. These areas within a range show the first signs of overgrazing and deterioration (Fig. 134). In range terminology, this pattern of grazing is recognized as poor distribution of range use.

Seldom is it possible to find ranges that are stocked year long, regardless of size, with grazing management left to the livestock, that are producing anywhere near the potential on all parts of that range. Valleys, smooth mesas, areas near water, south slopes, or some portion of that range will invariably be overgrazed.

This has been the fate of many acres of rangeland where open range-free choice management is practiced. The more accessible and perhaps better sites have received abusive grazing use and have declined in range condition. Many of these sites have deteriorated beyond feasible restoration, as indicated by severe erosion, brush invasion, and near complete destruction of the range.

DEFERRED GRAZING

In its strictest sense, deferred grazing is the vacating or non-use of a grazing unit from the beginning of growth until full plant development and seed maturity at or near the end of the growing season. Contrary to some viewpoints, deferment is not a loss of grazing use, since good forage plants will remain palatable and nutritious after maturity and dormancy occurs. This system of grazing management is designed to give the desirable forage plants full benefit of the entire growing season for maximum plant development (Fig. 135). Theoretically, those plants would have the advantage of all available growth requirements for full development during that undisturbed period. Some benefit will result to range plants from any deferment of 90 days or more during the growing season. Even though there is insufficient moisture for vegetative growth during such a period, deferment relieves the pressure and further deterioration of plants, including the root system.

In spite of the generally achieved benefits from deferred grazing

Fig. 135. A range deferred during the growing season permits plants to fully develop. This not only adds to total production but gives strength and stability to the range. (Photo courtesy U.S. Soil Conservation Service, Texas.)

as applied according to seasonal periods, the specific needs of the range should be evaluated as a basis for application of the practice. For example, a range may have reached a stage of deterioration where undesirable or even noxious plants are in greater abundance than the grasses that are to be improved. Deferment of that range from the first of May through October may result in further depletion of the desirable grass as a result of competition from the undesirable vegetation that has also benefited from the deferment. On the other hand, the desired benefit may result from a period of 30 to 45 days concentrated or heavy grazing early in the growing season. Thus, much of the competition to the plants to be improved would have been removed both by grazing and trampling. Such improvement would, however, be predicated on the palatability of the undesirable plants and, of utmost importance, complete deferment of the area immediately following that grazing period. Under this management, the desirable vegetation would respond more fully in the shorter period of deferment with competing plants removed than during the full growth season with the competition.

There are also ranges that are of good quality and very productive, with a kind of vegetation that is most nutritious and palatable only during the spring and early summer months. Generally, this type of vegetation will respond to fall deferment by growth and maturity that will insure maintenance of the stand. Some of the bluestems and other tall and mid grasses are in this category.

These variations and exceptions to plant response from the practice of deferred grazing are not to discredit the practice but to point up the importance of evaluating the needs and best use of the range and results that might be expected. The practice of deferred grazing is recognized as one of the best systems of grazing management in use, but often it can be improved by slight modifications in application of the practice to fit local situations.

ROTATION GRAZING

Rotation grazing is a systematic schedule of moving livestock from one grazing unit or pasture to another, usually where more than two pastures are used. Such a system involves a rather fixed number of animals in a single herd, moved on the basis of a rather fixed schedule. The length of the grazing period and that of subsequent rest periods is usually based on the time required for the rested pasture to make adequate regrowth for its subsequent grazing period.

This intensity of management is seldom justifiable on a range operation. Range grasses do not normally respond quickly enough nor can they be given supplemental treatment to insure their response for such a system. Seldom is it feasible to manage range livestock in a system of this intensity.

Because of these limitations, this practice of grazing management is hardly ever used for range operations, but it may have limited use where comparatively small and uniform pastures are available. It is especially well-suited where pasture treatment and management are feasible. Pasture renovation, mowing for weed control, irrigation, and the use of fertilizers are often supplemental practices to grazing management for high production where a rotation system is used.

ROTATION-DEFERRED GRAZING SYSTEMS

Rotation-deferred grazing systems are, as the name implies, a combination of the principles of deferred grazing and rotation grazing. However, only with appropriate modifications and combinations of those practices are they practical for ranch operations.

Rotation-deferred systems of grazing for rangelands of the southwest are credited to Dr. Leo B. Merrill, of the Texas Agricultural Research Station located at Sonora, Texas. His work was initiated in 1949 and will continue as long as valuable information, both as to range forage production and livestock production, is being accumulated.

The original work on these systems involved four pastures of approximately equal size and equal quality in regard to the forage resource. The system has been put into use on numerous ranches, especially in Texas, where procedures and benefits are well known (Figs. 136 and 137).

Modifications of the four-pasture system have been made whereby three-pasture and two-pasture systems can be used with success. This step has made it possible to initiate a grazing management system on many ranches where the country or fencing arrangements do not lend themselves to the four-pasture system.

Results to date from rotation-deferred systems of grazing have been remarkably good, both from the standpoint of range improvement and livestock production. Dr. Merrill's work was initiated with a stocking rate of 32 animal units per section, using a combination of three kinds of livestock, cattle, sheep, and goats. Once the system was underway, the grazing value of each pasture began to show an increase which was consistent even through a period of seven years of below average rainfall. After fifteen years, the stocking rate was conservatively estimated at 45 animal units per section by a group of experienced range technicians. In addition to beneficial results for domestic livestock, deer have shown a preference for these pastures and have used them at an increasing rate each year.

To briefly describe these systems of rotation deferment, the four-pasture system, as implied, is four pastures in proximity to one another and as comparable as possible as to size, kind of country, and grazing value. The combined number of animal units for the four pastures is determined. This combined herd is then divided into three equal herds and placed into three of the pastures. The grazing

Fig. 136. This is one pasture in a rotation-deferred grazing system in the Hill Country of Texas. Both the use and rest periods come at a different season in successive years, to the benefit of various kinds of vegetation on different range sites. (Photo courtesy U.S. Soil Conservation Service, Texas.)

Fig. 137. The four-pasture rotation-deferred system is effective on any kind of range. This sandy land range on the F. H. McQuiddy ranch in the Texas Panhandle has responded to the system, along with sand sage control. (Photo courtesy U.S. Soil Conservation Service, Texas.)

schedule is based on a four-month cycle. At the end of four months, one herd is moved to the pasture that has received the four-month rest or deferment. At the end of the next four-month period, one herd is moved from another of the nondeferred pastures into the one just having had the four-month deferment. This cycle is continued year after year, making what may be considered a unit of management for that ranch.

By this system, a pasture is actually grazed twelve months and then rested four months. However, each successive rest period comes at a different season of the year during a three-year period. This provides periodic seasonal growth requirement benefits to the complex composition of the vegetation that usually prevails on any good range. The chart in Fig. 138 shows the application of this system.

When a four-pasture system of rotation-deferred grazing is not feasible and three pastures or two pastures are available, they too can be worked into a satisfactory system. Here again, the combined total number of animal units for all pastures would be determined. Where three pastures are in the system, the number of animal units would be divided into two equal herds. Where only two pastures are involved in the system, only one herd would be maintained.

A three-month grazing cycle has proved quite satisfactory for both the three-pasture and the two-pasture systems. However, from the practical angle, two of the three-month periods are combined in alternate use and rest periods. Also, the two-pasture system may be applied on a four-month cycle, alternating equal use and rest periods between the two pastures. This latter system has been referred to as the four-by-four system for two pastures.

The chart in Fig. 139 is a tabular description of the three-pasture and the four-pasture rotation-deferred systems with the months column filled in according to appropriate periods for a feasible grazing program. The chart in Fig. 140 is a tabular description of two applications of the two-pasture system that are feasible.

Other rotation-deferred systems have been developed, and others will be developed to fit local conditions over the country. For example, E. William Anderson, State Range Conservationist, Soil Conservation Service, Portland, Oregon, reports on rotation of deferred grazing for ranges where summer grazing is available on nonrange-land. This represents conditions that exist in the Pacific Northwest. Systems are in use where only spring, summer, and fall use is made of the range. These systems usually involve rest periods for a pasture

Fig. 138

THE FOUR-PASTURE ROTATION-DEFERRED
GRAZING SYSTEM

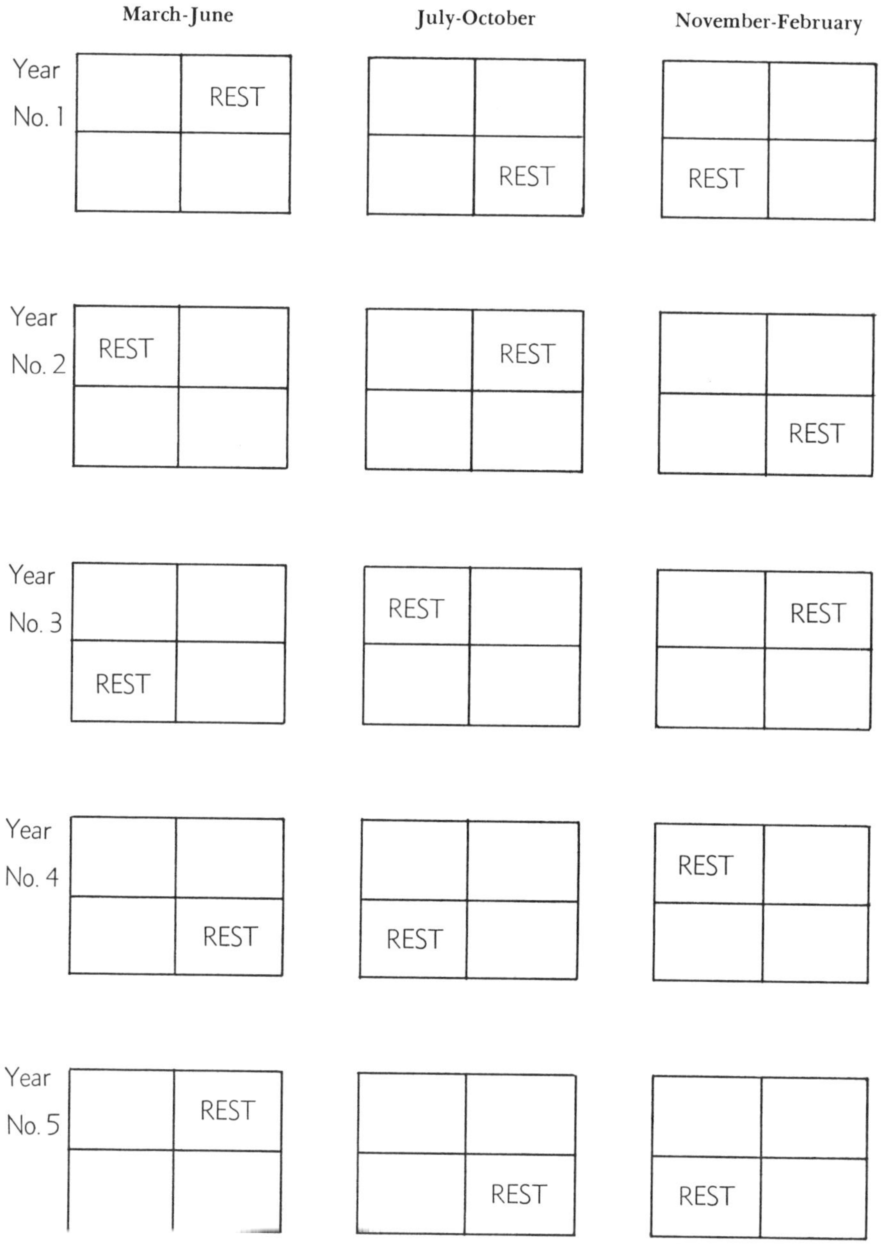

Fig. 139

GRAZING SCHEDULES FOR ROTATION-DEFERRED SYSTEMS OF GRAZING

Three-Pasture System (Graze Two Herds) — Pastures

Months*	No. 1	No. 2	No. 3
May			
June	REST	GR.	
July			GR.
Aug.		REST	
Sept.			
Oct.	GR.		
Nov.			
Dec.			REST
Jan.		GR.	
Feb.			
Mar.	REST		
Apr.			GR.
May			
June		REST	
July	GR.		
Aug.			
Sept.			REST
Oct.		GR.	
Nov.			
Dec.	REST		
Jan.			GR.
Feb.			
Mar.		REST	
Apr.	GR.		
May			
June			REST
July		GR.	
Aug.			
Sept.	REST		
Oct.			GR.
Nov.			
Dec.		REST	
Jan.	GR.		
Feb.			
Mar.		GR.	REST
Apr.			

Four-Pasture System (Graze Three Herds) — Pastures

Months*	No. 1	No. 2	No. 3	No. 4
Oct.				
Nov.		REST	GR.	
Dec.				
Jan.				GR.
Feb.				
Mar.	GR.		REST	
Apr.				
May				
June				
July		GR.		REST
Aug.				
Sept.				
Oct.				
Nov.	REST		GR.	
Dec.				
Jan.				
Feb.				
Mar.		REST		GR.
Apr.				
May				
June				
July	GR.		REST	
Aug.				
Sept.				
Oct.				
Nov.		GR.		REST
Dec.				
Jan.				
Feb.				
Mar.	REST		GR.	
Apr.				
May				GR.
June				
July	GR.	REST		
Aug.				
Sept.				

*List months starting with the month the system is to be initiated. Disregard calendar years.

Fig. 140

GRAZING SCHEDULES FOR ROTATION-DEFERRED SYSTEMS OF GRAZING

Two-Pasture Switchback System (Graze One Herd) **Pastures**			Two-Pasture Four-by-Four System (Graze One Herd) **Pastures**		
Months*	No. 1	No. 2	Months*	No. 1	No. 2
June July Aug.	REST	GR.	Nov. Dec. Jan. Feb.	GR.	REST
Sept. Oct. Nov. Dec. Jan. Feb.	GR.	REST	Mar. Apr. May June	REST	GR.
Mar. Apr. May	REST	GR.	July Aug. Sept. Oct.	GR.	REST
June July Aug.	GR.	REST	Nov. Dec. Jan. Feb.	REST	GR.
Sept. Oct. Nov. Dec. Jan. Feb.	REST	GR.	Mar. Apr. May June	GR.	REST
Mar. Apr. May	GR.	REST	July Aug. Sept. Oct.	REST	GR.
June July Aug.	REST	GR.	Nov. Dec. Jan. Feb.	GR.	REST
Sept. Oct. Nov. Dec. Jan. Feb.	GR.	REST	Mar. Apr. May June	REST	GR.
Mar. Apr May	REST	GR.	July Aug. Sept. Oct.	GR	REST

*List months starting with the month the system is to be initiated. Disregard calendar years.

during the first half of the growing season one year and the last half the following year. Such a system can be used where only two pastures are available of reasonably comparable grazing values; or three or four pastures may be included in the system.

Although the use of rotation-deferred systems of grazing does intensify ranching operations, they have proved their value in improved range conditions and increased production from rangeland. The point cannot be emphasized too strongly, however, that rotation-deferred grazing systems are of little value on a hit or miss basis. They must be planned for timely and systematic application and usually require two or three years before benefits are in evidence. This does not mean, however, that there is no flexibility in these systems. Adverse weather, economic reverses, or other conditions may make it imperative that a system be interrupted for a season or sometimes longer. When this becomes necessary, the system, as planned, should be resumed at the earliest possible time. When resumed, it is important that the system be reinstated as to both the livestock numbers and the pastures as of the date of reinstatement, according to the original plan. To resume the system where it left off at the time of the interruption would not only complicate the system but likely would result in unscheduled and perhaps abusive use of one or more pastures.

SEASONAL SUITABILITY SYSTEM

Much of the rangeland of the west, and particularly the southwest, has a rainfall pattern that is very low and undependable. This characteristic, along with many years of excessive grazing, has greatly depleted and in fact changed much of the range to something quite different from what it was originally (Fig. 141). This is evident where grass is almost non-existent and creosotebush, tarbush, or other desert shrubs cover the landscape, or, where there was once a good mixture of grasses that has given way to a near pure stand of tobosa grass, a seasonal forage plant. Also, many ranges have changed from sparse stands of perennial grasses to the production of annual vegetation, and then only in years or seasons of very favorable rainfall.

These conditions have imposed a type of grazing system that K. A. Valentine developed when with the Department of Animal, Range

Fig. 141. A sandy loam range in an 8-inch rainfall. After eight years of good management, only scattered plants of dropseed and threeawn are to be found. On occasional years of good spring rainfall, weeds make good, short seasonal grazing.

and Wildlife Science at New Mexico State University. It is identified as a seasonal suitability system of grazing management. Valentine recognizes such a system as the only productive use that can be made of these ranges. This type of country is not reliable enough for a predetermined plan such as a rotation-deferred system, which requires that ranges be usable at any season.

There are two primary objectives of the seasonal suitability system of grazing: to use the vegetation that is produced when it is available, palatable, and nutritious; and to not use the more-desirable plants that might be present in small quantities at the time or season when they need every advantage of growth requirements to maintain and improve the quality of that range. To achieve these management objectives generally requires a type of ranching operation that is quite flexible and somewhat unstable. An exception might be the rancher who plans specifically for the necessary and immediate adjustments in livestock management. For the range that produces only annual vegetation in good seasons, livestock must be quickly accessible and equally as quickly removed when the feed resource is gone. Likewise, for the range with only a sparse stand of a desirable grass that is seasonally palatable and nutritious, such as black grama for winter use and tobosa grass for spring and early summer use, livestock must be readily available at the time of range readiness and conveniently removed at the crucial time.

This system of management is being used satisfactorily in low-rainfall areas that are susceptible to drought periods that may be seasonal or may extend over a period of several years. Operations in these areas are, of necessity, either the "in and out of business" type or are quite extensive in scope and often include other resources than the country of seasonal suitability range.

HIGH-INTENSITY-LOW-FREQUENCY SYSTEM OF GRAZING

A recent innovation in grazing management, still in its early stages of development, is a system devised by the Texas A & M University Agricultural Experiment Station. The system is markedly different from all previous concepts of grazing management. It provides for extremely high intensities and degrees of grazing range forage. But any degree of overuse is more than compensated for by the frequency and short grazing period involved.

The system is identified and referred to by the descriptive terms by which it is known: a high-intensity-low-frequency grazing system, abbreviated HILF.

The general idea of the system is to concentrate livestock in a single pasture in sufficient numbers to near completely utilize all usable forage in a period of thirty days or less. When the best grazing is gone, the animals are moved to another pasture in the multi-pasture system. There will be enough pastures in the system that returning to the first pasture grazed will be no sooner than five months. Even a longer period of time may be desirable if there are a sufficient number of pastures to make it possible.

Results to date are striking as to livestock production without damage to the range. This system is in use with a high degree of success in Africa and Rhodesia.

Work thus far in Texas indicates that production may be as much as three times that from any other system of continuous grazing.

This, coupled with greatly reduced overhead costs by more concentrated livestock handling and management, can increase returns per acre or per animal unit far above that from systems involving season-long or year-long use of the range. And this is in face of recognized initial increased costs for additional fencing and handling facilities.

This HILF system is one with great promise, and it will, no doubt, have much greater application to the range country than might be recognized at the outset.

GRAZING SYSTEMS A MUST

Grazing systems geared to the growth and production requirements of both the livestock and the forage resource are the only salvation to continued productive use of millions of acres of rangeland. It is unfortunate but true that the livestock people moved out 25 years or more ahead of the grass people in improving the quality and production of their product. Even more serious is the fact that the range resources of the country were on a decided downward trend and state of deterioration. This simply means that trend must be halted, reversed, and the needed improvement in the range resource made.

Too many ranchers, as well as commercial interests, are looking for the magic wand to solve the problems of the range country. Certainly there is a need and a place for practically everything that has come along thus far. Methods of brush and weed control, range seeding methods and equipment, soil and water conservation programs, and many other innovations have contributed their part in the restoration and maintenance of our rangelands.

With all of these, good as they are, there is nothing to take the place of the proper grazing use and management of the forage plants placed on our rangelands under the stewardship of man. Every living thing has not only its purpose but its requirements for existence. Grazing management is man's responsibility and so is the willingness to provide those requirements.

Grazing management systems are only the skills and the perseverance of man to fulfill his obligation in this respect. Even though the use of a grazing management system may impose some restrictions on a ranch operator, as compared to the free and easy way of the open range, it is not without many compensating benefits—benefits to the ranching operation as well as to the forage resource. Improved quantity and quality of the range forage simply adds to livestock production. A third to half of the pastures vacated in a deferred rotation system save labor, time, and possibly upkeep for that period. More cattle for a shorter period of time in a pasture result in more dispersion of animals and better distribution of grazing. Seasonal adjustments in grazing use benefit the vegetation by preventing selective and continuous use of certain choice plants until they are destroyed. These and many other benefits and advantages to grazing management systems are to be had by the ranch operator who wants to preserve and improve his range resource and sustain his operation in a satisfying and productive way.

Chapter 16

ENVIRONMENTAL AND MANAGEMENT
INFLUENCES ON RANGE PRODUCTION

Total production from all plants—a measure of the potential forage production of a range. Production of nongrazable versus grazable plants accounted for by efficient management. Influences that cause range forage production to fluctuate. Plant competition and forage yields. Evaluating competitive yields. Measuring range forage yields as a basis for production and management judgments. Estimating range yields as a practical management tool. Stocking ranges on the basis of yield information.

In considering range production, it is necessary to take into account all vegetation that is present, including grasses, weeds, brush, and trees. Each of these groups of plants has an effect on range production. They either enter into the total production of usable forage, or they affect forage production because of the competition they create to other forage producing plants.

In range management it is important to recognize the differences between total production of all types of vegetation growing on the range and the production of those forage plants that will be grazed and converted to livestock products. Planned grazing management can result in the utilization of some plants that normally would not be grazed. Seasonal adjustments in grazing, better distribution of grazing, or using the kinds of livestock best suited to the range are examples of management principles that can be applied to get the most grazing from a range.

But even with the best of range management, it is seldom possible to obtain full utilization of all range plants. This is particularly true of ranges that have deteriorated to a fair or poor range condition with much of the production being from low-quality plants. This is also true on ranges that have natural stands of unpalatable, poor quality plants. Examples are ranges of the semi-arid southwest, as well as other range types throughout the country, that support sparse to dense stands of desert shrub and other woody plants with no grazing value.

When these conditions exist, the rancher is confronted with a production problem that is reflected directly in the net return from his ranching operation. Although the most significant example that presently confronts the ranching industry is that of brush invasion onto rangeland, the problem is by no means limited to brush. Regardless of the part of the country being considered, there are always range plants, including some grasses, that are passed over by animals grazing the range. To the extent this occurs it is a wastage of the potential range resource.

Not only is it important to the rancher to know this is taking place on his range, it is equally important for him to know why it is taking place. Knowing what is happening, and why, would be an incentive for him to do everything possible and feasible to convert otherwise wasted production to usable range forage.

These differences in production of forage plants and those plants that will not be grazed should identify grazing management needs. These determinations would include evaluation of the grazing unit or pasture, important range sites, and important plants that will be used and those that will not be used, under conditions of current management. Such evaluation procedures are in contrast to the usual "acres per cow" basis, or the sometimes irresponsible criterion of stocking as long as there is any grass to be seen regardless of whether or not it is grazable.

RANGE FORAGE PRODUCTION WILL FLUCTUATE

Within any climatic zone, production from rangeland has a limited potential. From this potential there will be natural variations as influenced by such factors as kind of soil, topography, soil-water relations, and other characteristics of different range sites. There will be other variations, both as to total production and production of usable forage, even on a single site. These differences are brought about primarily by changes in range condition. As stated in Chapter 5, range yields are not the criterion for range condition. It is generally true, however, that range yields, particularly that of usable forage, will decline as the range condition declines from excellent to good, fair, and poor.

With specific reference to forage production, which is the primary objective in range management, fluctuations will occur from one year to the next. Of several possible reasons for such fluctuations, climatic deviations from the normal is basically the underlying cause. With below-normal rainfall at the season of maximum plant growth, production will decline accordingly. Lower yields will vary from slightly less than normal to essentially no production in a drought period. Conversely, with above-normal rainfall, forage yields will increase, but only to the extent the health and vigor of the plants will permit. With a good, vigorous stand of forage plants, production will reach the maximum growth possible for the kinds of plants in the composition. In contrast, if plants have become weakened by abusive grazing use, with little or no bud development and little or no stored plant food, production from those plants will be but slightly increased regardless of the amount of rainfall. In fact, weakened plants will produce all they are capable of on much less than normal rainfall for any locality.

Fig. 142. On poor condition ranges, even with above-normal rainfall, forage production is far below the potential of the site.

A concrete example of this kind of plant reaction to rainfall was evidenced in the very favorable year, from the standpoint of moisture, of 1941. At a location in west central Texas the average annual rainfall is 19.83 inches. In 1941 the total rainfall was 32.67 inches, with an adequate amount falling during the spring and early summer when plants make maximum growth. With this increased amount of rainfall, forage yields on overused and low-condition ranges was no greater than during any year of normal or even below-normal rainfall (Fig. 142). On the other hand, ranges with these same rainfall conditions that had not been abusively grazed in the past and were improving to a higher condition produced as much as 40 per cent more forage than they would be expected to yield with normal rainfall (Fig. 143). Comparable results were found throughout the range country regardless of the kind of grass.

Fig. 143. Ranges in a relatively high condition are in shape to make efficient use of above-normal rainfall with increased production.

It should be pointed out that the 1941–42 era was one of those life savers that comes along once each decade or so. In spite of the fact that production was not generally increased in 1941, the year of the highest rainfall on record, 1942 was a year of increased production with no more than normal rainfall. This fact is attributed to nothing more than an improved condition of range plants during the previous favorable year, when management would permit. Along with just fair production from the more-desirable range plants in their weakened condition in 1941 was an above-normal production of the less-desirable grasses and forbs common to lower condition ranges. And, too, with very favorable moisture conditions, these "junk" plants did furnish a more than usual amount of grazing and over a much longer period of time. This took a great deal of pressure off the better plants, allowing them to improve in strength and vigor, thus the increased production in 1942.

WHEN THE RAIN COMES IS IMPORTANT

Of equal importance in range management, when the rain comes has much to do with forage yields. When there is an adequate amount of soil moisture to stimulate plant development at the normal time when temperatures are right, plant growth will start. If an adequate moisture supply is continued through the growing season, normal production in accordance with the health of the plants may be expected. On the other hand, if moisture is inadequate at the time for beginning plant growth, forage production will be reduced. Lowered yields will correspond to the length of time available moisture is delayed.

If moisture becomes available within the first two or three weeks after time for plant growth to start, near-normal production may be expected. However, if available moisture is delayed until near or after the mid-point of the growing season, forage production will be greatly reduced, regardless of the condition of the range or the plants involved. This phenomenon was discussed in Chapter 3. Briefly, if grass plants are healthy, during the early stages of growth much production is in the form of foliage—leaves and stems. After the mid-point of the growing season, the plant then expends its growth energy to the development of its reproduction processes, namely, fruiting parts and seed. When, for any reason, normal growth con-

Fig. 144. Rain was delayed until about September 1, to produce this crop of blue grama. Total forage production was only 650 pounds per acre when clipped at crown level, and consisted of seed stems, seed heads, and very short leaves. (Photo courtesy U.S. Soil Conservation Service, Texas.)

ditions do not occur, and the lack of moisture is a primary cause, plant growth will be altered. If rain comes late in the season, by hormone action all growth buds will be converted to the process of reproduction, in an attempt by the plant to perpetuate itself. In this process, only seed forming stems will be formed and leaf growth will be reduced to a minimum; thus, food manufacturing processes of the plant are greatly reduced.

All too often this latter type of growth is deceiving to the casual observer. There will be a good amount of seed stem and seed head development, giving the appearance of a normal production for the year (Fig. 144). The deception is the lack of volume and weight of the yield. With good stands of grass with average or above vitality, and with ample rainfall coming in late summer, blue grama ranges have been found to produce not more than 25 per cent of a normal yield. And these have been total yields for the year, including the entire plant development of stems, leaves, and seed. When, with proper use, no more than 50 per cent of the production is used, it means that only 12½ per cent of a normal total forage production is available for safe grazing use. When a fixed stocking rate of so many acres per animal is used, there obviously will be a shortage of feed, certainly overuse, and very likely abusive use of the range.

PLANT COMPETITION AND FORAGE YIELDS

Forage production on any kind of rangeland is dependent on three basic criteria: an adequate supply of plant food material; sufficient available moisture for maximum plant development; and plenty of room to fully develop a root system and the vegetative structure of the plant. The first two criteria are essential to life itself in the plant; the third is primarily the regulator of production. A strong root system will support maximum vegetative growth, since the two are always about equal in volume. Therefore, for maximum growth and production, every plant must have room to spread its root system throughout the working depth of the soil (Fig. 145). A strong root system is necessary to meet the competition of other root systems that are ready and waiting to take over the entire root zone. Of no less importance is adequate room for the above-ground or vegetative parts of the plant to develop fully (Fig. 146). Competition for space above ground in the area of plant growth becomes acute under many and varied circumstances. A tree growing close to a building will develop but few branches next to the structure, and they will always be dwarfed and conform only to the space allowed for them. Trees or shrubs growing thickly in a stand become spindly, with few branches, all of which extend straight upward, striving for space in which to grow. And so it is with grass and other forage plants in a stand. If the stand is too thick, and especially if much of it consists of less-desirable plants, competition for aerial space actually becomes a limiting factor in production.

This is true even with a dense stand of a single species of grass, regardless of how good or how poor it is. With range grasses, it is a mistake to think that the more dense the stand the higher the pro-

Fig. 145. To insure maximum vegetative production, there must be plenty of room in the root zone for full development of the root system. (Photo courtesy U.S. Soil Conservation Service, Texas.)

Fig. 146. For highest forage yields, plants must have room to fully develop. Plants properly spaced for a particular climate will produce more than a dense stand of that same grass. (Photo courtesy U.S. Soil Conservation Service, Texas.)

duction. This misconception is perhaps more prevalent with a blue grama-buffalograss mixture than on almost any other kind of range. In the first place, buffalograss is a turf grass. Heavy grazing or close mowing causes it to form a dense turf. Close grazing of blue grama in the mixture results in it also contributing to the density of the turf. Thus, a range that has the appearance of a lawn usually lacks most of the growth requirements for high production. Such ranges seldom produce more than 50 per cent as much forage as they would if adjusted to a healthy stand and with growing space less severely limited. Competition for food, water, air, light, and space is a serious deterrent to range forage production.

A situation as just described may also be misinterpreted from another standpoint, that is, the matter of annual weed competition coming into a dense stand of grass. It is not uncommon for dense stands to permit very heavy invasion of weeds. Many ranges of the southwest are highly vulnerable to invasion of such weeds as annual broomweed (*gutierrezia dracunculoides*). This invasion is possible for two reasons, even in dense stands as described above. First, the seeds germinate in the fall when there is no severe competition from the grass, especially if it is closely grazed. Second, with a lawnlike stand of short grass, the root system of the grass will also be rather dense but very short. Eighty per cent of the roots will be in the top 2 to 4 inches of soil. Thus, the shallow root system affords little or no competition with the deeply penetrated tap root of the broom weed.

Because of these production limitations, a most important facet in range management is permitting the most-desirable plants of a range to become healthy and vigorous and adjust themselves to the most-productive stand possible. In this way they will be able to offer the strongest possible competition and resistance to other plants that will invade the range when given a chance.

In many areas, competition from brush and noxious weeds that invade ranges is perhaps the most serious problem confronting ranchers. On many ranges there are from one to many obnoxious species to contend with. Generally, this type of plant gets a foothold once range deterioration starts as a result of overuse, drought, or possibly a combination of these two adversities. Without careful management of such ranges, these plants will continue to invade or increase, often at a very rapid rate. Examples of such invasion to near exclusion of profitable ranching are the mixed brush invasions of south Texas (Fig. 147); mesquite over much of the southwest range country (Fig. 148); sand sagebrush and shinnery oak on sandy ranges of the Southern Plains (Fig. 149); scrub oak on hilly and mountainous ranges (Fig. 150); yucca on sandy loam sites of the southwest (Fig. 151); broom snakeweed on both mountainous and plains ranges (Fig. 152); creosotebush on desert ranges of the southwest; and numerous other species, including some that are extremely poisonous, have taken over much of the rangelands of the west. This problem is not limited to western ranges. Lands used for grazing purposes in the eastern half of the U.S. are also subject to this type of range deterioration. In those areas, however, woody invaders in particular usually consist of re-infestation and regrowth of tree and shrub species that were climax to the area. They were removed through harvest of wood products or for other land uses but are no longer maintained as such.

The influences that invading plants have on forage production are

Fig. 147. Mixed brush invasion has completely changed the type of range production on many acres of rangeland, especially in warmer climates. (Photo courtesy U.S. Soil Conservation Service, Texas.)

Fig. 148. Mesquite invasion on rangelands of the southwest poses a most serious range forage production problem. (Photo courtesy U.S. Soil Conservation Service, Texas.)

Fig. 149. The increase of sand sagebrush and sand shinnery oak on southern plains sandy land ranges has seriously affected production. (Photo courtesy U.S. Soil Conservation Service, Texas.)

Fig. 150. Scrub oak on many hilly and mountain ranges is a difficult brush species to control. It greatly reduces range production. (Photo courtesy U.S. Soil Conservation Service, Texas.)

Fig. 151. Yucca on sandy loam range sites crowds out grass and greatly reduces the yield of the grass that is left. (Photo courtesy U.S. Soil Conservation Service, Texas.)

Fig. 152. Broom snakeweed, a perennial, has invaded and seriously depleted thousands of acres of good rangeland. (Photo courtesy U.S. Soil Conservation Service, Texas.)

many and varied. The more vigorous and robust those invading plants are the more serious the effect on range forage yields. Brush invasion results in near-complete occupancy of the land where it grows. It overshadows lower growing forage plants, taking the room they need and excluding sunlight. The root system may completely dominate the root zone needed by grassplants. With these physical advantages, brush can maintain near-complete domination of all elements needed for forage production. To illustrate, blue grama in a semi-arid climate requires approximately 560 pounds of water to produce 1 pound of grass (air dry). In contrast, approximately 2,100 pounds of water will be used in producing 1 pound of mesquite (air dry). Plant food requirements of woody plants are utilized in the same relative proportion. These adverse reactions, along with the room and shading problem, clearly portray the competitive effect on brush infested ranges.

EVALUATING COMPETITIVE INFLUENCES OF RANGE PLANTS

It is impossible to evaluate a range or range production without knowing, within reasonable limits, the kind of plants that are present. Even with a range that supports nothing but grasses with no weed or woody invaders, it is important to know what the grasses are. Seldom does a range exist with only a single species of grass, but if such does occur, an evaluation is very simple. However, when two or more grasses are in the mixture, there will likely be differences in the grazing values of each grass. Palatability, nutritive quality, season of growth and development, or some difference will affect the use and management of that range. To be most efficient, grazing use and management must be based on the grazing value of the forage at hand.

With experience, a reasonably accurate estimate can be made on a percentage basis, of the amounts of various kinds of plants in the composition. A trained technician may well make such estimates to within 5 to 10 per cent of accuracy as determined by recognized measuring procedures.

Composition estimates can be made with a higher degree of accuracy if dealt with in small representative areas of the range. Areas of a square yard, square meter, or even a square foot are easily measured and interpreted to acre yields. The smaller the unit, however, the greater the number of samples that should be taken to be representative. As a self training procedure, the individual should start by examining a comparatively small unit, such as the square foot. Within such an area each different kind of plant can be recognized and compared in quantity with every other kind of plant in that area. As a gauge to sharpen his judgment, he may measure with a ruler the diameter of each plant crown at ground level and record his findings. Or, he may make a measurement and a judgment as to surface area covered in square inches. By whatever unit of measure used, a fairly accurate determination can be made as to the percentage each plant makes of the whole, or 100 per cent of the area.

To be more precise in making this type evaluation of plant competition, actual measurement can be resorted to for the percentage value of each species. The procedure commonly used by range technicians involves establishing the plot as a square foot or square yard and then measuring each plant crown, as near ground level as possible. This is done by lightly compressing the plant crown between the thumb and first finger. The distance between the thumb and finger is measured with a rule, calibrated in easily read units. Readings in hundredths of a foot are easily handled. The values for each species are added to get the total for that species. The sum of all species is the total, or 100 per cent of the vegetation in the plot. Dividing this figure into the total for each species gives the per cent that species represents in the composition.

This procedure is used to evaluate range areas for purposes other than species composition. Range forage yields by species may be determined by the use of small plots. The size of the plot may or may not be significant, depending on how uniform and representative it is of the area. In some instances, square yard or square meter plots are best; in sparse vegetation, larger plots may be more desirable. For some situations, square foot plots in greater numbers and more widely distributed over the area being analyzed may be most representative.

The line transect or line intercept is also used for more-accurate evaluation of range vegetation. A line extended across the area to be analyzed by use of a chain, wire, or heavy cord is commonly used, and a steel tape calibrated to easily identified units of measure is most convenient.

This procedure is accomplished with the chain stretched at a height that will permit vegetative parts of all plants in the composition to intercept the chain. The longer the line, the more reliable the information gathered. A hundred-foot line is considered a very reliable index to the value of most areas being studied. With the hundred-foot line, and with calibrations in hundredths of a foot, percentage readings can be made directly.

To evaluate vegetation along a line transect, each individual plant is listed and the distance on the line it occupies is recorded. When this is done for each and every plant that intercepts the line, values are totaled and converted to per cent for each species. This represents the species composition for the area the same as was determined by the plot method.

Procedures such as the plot and the line transect are very important, along with others that have been developed, for scientific purposes. For the layman, their value and importance are in the training and sharpening of judgment for making reliable estimates of range condition and range management needs. From such training and with experience it is not difficult to make reasonably accurate range composition judgments of forage plants. Judgment estimates of species other than forage will be discussed later in this chapter.

MEASURING RANGE FORAGE YIELDS

A reasonably accurate estimate of forage yields or projected yields is the most important criterion for sound range management planning. Regardless of the several other important factors, it is pounds of range forage available that permits good management of both the range and the livestock.

Scientists have developed numerous procedures for accurately measuring vegetation to determine yields. By utilizing these techniques, much valuable information has been obtained relative to range yields, range use, and plant management. Scientific procedures and techniques cannot be duplicated in practical range management. However, techniques that are practical have been patterned from them that serve well in making reliable yield determinations.

Through the history of the ranching industry, range yields have been measured in terms of numbers of animals or pounds of animal products. Although this is the end product from range yields, there is really no reliable way to interpret these yields into either current or sustained production from the range. On the other hand, range production in terms of pounds of usable forage can be interpreted into livestock production in whatever unit of measure desired. Furthermore, production from overuse of the range or from unreliable "junk" plants that would signify range deterioration should not enter into projected yields.

Range forage yields per acre, the most logical known criterion, can be determined rather easily for practical purposes. On open grassland, clipping forage from representative plots that can be converted to an acre basis will give reliable yield data. If the area being evaluated is not an open stand of range forage, but has areas of tree and brush growth, rock outcrops, or areas that are otherwise inaccessible to grazing, those areas should be eliminated when per acre grazing values are being determined, since they are not supporting grazable forage. This is best done by making a per cent cut of the area involved, preferably after the full acre yield determination has been made.

The extent of areas of obstruction from grazing may be arrived at by sample measurements, estimates based on sample transects over the range, aerial photographs, if available, or any other method by which the evaluator can make a sound judgment.

SIZE OF PLOTS AND WEIGHT CONVERSIONS

The size of the plot to be used in making yield evaluations should be determined by such factors as uniformity of area; density or sparseness of the vegetation; kind of vegetation; and time and facilities for making the evaluation. Just how the evaluation is to be made will depend on the objective in mind. It may be a total vegetative production; it may be the yield based on a degree of harvest commensurate with proper grazing use; it may be the production of various kinds or classes of vegetation.

Whatever the purpose, the size of the plot should be such that conversion to an acre basis can be done with ease. Therefore, plots calibrated to a fraction of an acre are best. The following table gives dimensions for fractional acre values.

Clippings from these size plots can be readily converted to acre yields by simple multiplication to raise the fraction to a whole number. Generally, to be consistent in weight yields, some degree of

TABLE 4
Plot Sizes for Fractions of an Acre[1]

ACRE VALUES	SIZE OF PLOT (FEET ON A SIDE)
1	208.7
1/2	147.6
1/4	104.35
1/10	66.0
1/20	46.6
1/50	29.5
1/100	20.87
1/200	14.75
1/400	10.43
1/1000	6.6
1/2000	4.67
1/4000	3.3

uniformity as to moisture content of the vegetation is desirable. It is commonly accepted that reduction of moisture to air dry conditions is reliable and practical.

Although little has been done to establish a reliable index for relative moisture content levels for range plants, some guidance has been furnished as a result of plant analysis work. Clipping studies by the Soil Conservation Service and findings of other agency research indicate that, as a general guide, moisture content of actively growing and near-fully developed grass plants is approximately 50 per cent of the total weight, that is, weight clipped at crown level of the plant and before noticeable wilting has taken place. In arid and semi-arid climates, with some species of grass, such as blue grama, hairy grama, and sand dropseed, the maximum moisture content has been found to be a little less than 50 per cent. As little as 43 per cent was found for these species from field studies by the Soil Conservation Service in southwest Texas.

Perhaps the most practical range forage yield determination procedure is that from the 9.6-square-foot plot. The shape of the plot is immaterial; it can be round, square, oblong, and can even be used for row plantings with different spacings between rows. The one basic requirement is that the area involved is 9.6 square feet, or a derivative of that area with correspondingly adjusted conversion factors.

[1] A. W. Sampson, Range and Pasture Management, 1923.

The basic concept for this procedure is to establish the plot to specifications (9.6 square feet), harvest the content of the plot, weigh in grams, and multiply the weight by 10. The result will be pounds per acre. To establish a square plot, it must be 3.1 feet on each side. A round plot of the required area must be 42 inches in diameter, or have a 21-inch radius. When scales are not available for recording weight in grams, conversions from weights in ounces can be made according to the following table:

TABLE 5
Conversion of Ounces to Grams

AREA	SIZE OF PLOT	MULTIPLY GRAMS BY	MULTIPLY OUNCES BY
1 sq. ft.	1 × 1 foot	96.0	2724.0
1 sq. meter	1 × 1 meter	8.92	253.1
9.6 sq. ft.	3.1 × 3.1 feet	10.0	283.5
1.91 sq. ft.	11½ × 24 inches	50.0	5224.5
10 sq. ft.	1 × 10 feet	9.6	272.4

For converting row samples to pounds per acre, the following equivalents can be used.

TABLE 6
Conversion of Raw Samples to Pounds per Acre

ROW SPACING	WIDTH OF A SINGLE ROW PLOT	LENGTH OF ROW SAMPLE	AREA OF PLOT (SQ. FT.)
42″	3.50′	2.75′	9.62
40″	3.33′	2.89′	9.62
38″	3.16′	3.04′	9.61
36″	3.00′	3.20′	9.60
24″	2.00′	4.80′	9.60
20″	1.67′	5.75′	9.60

In Table 6, weight of sample from row areas shown multiplied by 10, if in grams, or by 283.5, if in ounces, will give weight per acre in pounds.

Many other techniques and procedures have been developed and used for determining range yields. The method used is not important, provided reliable results are obtained. The importance of being able to make a reasonably accurate judgment of forage production cannot be overemphasized. The oversight of current yield information in favor of acres per head or head per section has doubtlessly been a strong contributor to range deterioration. Current values of range-land and the economics of livestock production strongly point to greater consideration of both production and utilization of range forage on an acre basis.

ESTIMATING RANGE YIELDS

It is not expected that ranchers and range managers will or should spend a great deal of time measuring range forage yields. This, however, does not preclude the desirability and in fact the near-necessity of their being knowledgeable about range yields. Forage production should be as important to them as livestock production. Through experience they have become proficient in judging livestock weights and gains. The same can be done by their forage production if they so desire. Furthermore, assistance in this endeavor is becoming available from technical people through various agricultural programs.

Through whatever source the information is available, it can readily become a part of the range manager's basic knowledge. It is important, however, to realize that this knowledge is not derived from a textbook. It is gained only through being on the land, walking on the vegetation and feeling it, and ultimately finding out what a given volume of it will weigh.

This experience enables vegetation to be looked at more objectively and in the perspective of volume and weight. This, in turn, will be related to various kinds of range and will ultimately be related to livestock production, and that is the achievement of the successful range manager.

Recent developments by the Soil Conservation Service in using individual representative plants as a basis for yield judgment shows great promise. This procedure is based on determining actual weight of individual plants in the composition of the range and relating that data to numbers of those plants within a prescribed area. From these estimates, per acre yields can be projected accurately.

A point in favor of this procedure is the fact it can be applied to tree and shrub production as well as ground cover. This is done by recognizing units of production of a single tree or shrub that can be quickly harvested and weighed. Such a unit would include a single representative branch or segment of the plant. The unit production can then be converted to the whole plant, which in turn can be converted to a per acre basis according to the number of plants per acre.

This procedure is most appropriately used to evaluate the current year's production rather than any accumulation of yield that might have taken place over the years. With experience and improvements in the unit weight procedure, it no doubt will become a practical and reliable tool in the field of range management.

STOCKING RATES BASED ON YIELD INFORMATION

Range forage yield information is the most reliable basis at hand for determining stocking rates for a range. However, if yield information is not tempered with the proper interpretations of other factors that enter in, errors in judgment can be made. Such factors might include how the forage is harvested; wastage through natural causes; and supplemental feed that might become available as annual plants in the spring, or even winter annuals in some areas.

Range forage is produced during the growing season for the dominant plants in the composition. Maximum production is at or near the end of the growing season and maturity of a major portion of the vegetation. If the total production could be harvested then and there, the yield would be the total production. Because the harvest of range forage by grazing animals must be extended throughout the year, or until a new crop is produced, maximum yield cannot be harvested. This compares favorably with a cultivated crop, such as sorghum or corn. If harvested at the stage of full development and maturity, the yield would be the maximum, but if harvest is delayed six or eight months, that maximum yield is no longer available.

The way animals graze, seasonal palatability and trampling through the winter months results in a nonconsumed use of a portion of the total production. An additional loss is deterioration of dormant plants. They naturally break down from repeated freezing and thawing. Heavy snow cover can cause some breakdown and compaction of plants, especially where a turf has developed. Excessive moisture adds to leaching as long as plants are active to any degree, and causes general deterioration of the structure of the plant. Wind will cause plants to break down, and they fall as litter or blow away during dry periods. Oxidation, a natural process in climatic influences on plants, will use some of the total forage produced. All these influences subtract from a total production when harvest must be extended through the dormant period of the range vegetation.

Over much of the southern and southwest range country, annual vegetation during the winter and spring months greatly influences the grazing capacity. Often this is a resource over and above what would be available from normally developed perennial vegetation on certain range sites.

An example of this type of production was found in Coleman County, Texas, during the making of flood control surveys in 1943. Stocking rate and production records of old timers revealed the fact that their ranges were as productive at the time of the survey as those same ranges were when operated by their fathers and grandfathers in the 1870's. This was in face of the fact that those ranges had greatly deteriorated from their original state of condition, especially along stream courses and valley sites. Those sites, being the most productive, had lost most of the original grasses they once supported. Moderate to very heavy infestations of mesquite and other brush species had occurred. Along with these changes, other grasses not originally present in the composition had moved in. These were primarily Texas wintergrass, a perennial that moved from the gulf coast northward, rescuegrass, and little barley, the latter two being annuals that also moved northward from more southerly climates. All these grasses are cool season; that is, they germinate and start growth in the fall, remaining green with some growth during the winter, then coming forth with an abundant production in spring and early summer with favorable moisture conditions.

It is this type of production that has maintained the grazing capacity of those ranges, even though the general range condition was, and, in too many instances continues to be, downward. This grazing resource need not necessarily be considered bad. In fact, it may even be superior to that with the original condition of the range because of the benefit from green forage during winter and early spring months. This greatly extends as well as improves the quality of the overall grazing season.

It is because of these variables in forage production that range yields must be realistic to be a reliable basis for determining stocking rates. But without a doubt, range forage yields reconciled to these variables by sound judgment and local experience do provide the most reliable basis for stocking a range. Furthermore, this is the information that is really basic to sound range management.

BIBLIOGRAPHY

BOOKS:

Allred, Burton W. *Practical Grassland Management.* Published By Sheep And Goat Raiser Magazine, San Angelo, Texas, 1950.

GOVERNMENT DOCUMENTS:

Federal:

Allred, B. W. *How To Classify Grasslands.* Range Fieldbook Service III, USDA Soil Conservation Service, Fort Worth, Texas, 1947.

Allred, B. W. *Progress In Perfecting Range Condition Classes.* USDA Soil Conservation Service, Fort Worth, Texas, 1947.

Bell, Hershel M., and V. M. Douglas. *Wartime Ranching In Texas And Oklahoma.* USDA Soil Conservation Service, Fort Worth, Texas, 1942.

Bell, Hershel M., and E. J. Dyksterhuis. *Regional Range Handbook.* USDA Soil Conservation Service, Fort Worth, Texas, 1944.

Chapline, W. R., and C. K. Cooperrider. *Climate And Grazing.* U. S. Forest Service, Yearbook of Agriculture, "Climate And Man," 1941.

Douglas, V. M. *Reports On Field Studies of Range Utilization.* USDA Soil Conservation Service, Fort Worth, Texas, 1942.

Leighly, John, Reed W. Bailey, C. Warren Thornthwaite, Glenn T. Trewortha, and Carl O. Sauer. *A Broad Classification Of Lands Of The United States.* Yearbook of Agriculture, "Climate and Man," 1941.

Leithead, Horace L. *Grass, How It Grows.* USDA Soil Conservation Service, Fort Worth, Texas, 1966.

Rechenthin, Clarence A. *Elementary Morphology of Grass Growth And How It Affects Utilization.* USDA Soil Conservation Service, Fort Worth, Texas, 1956.

Renner, Fredrick G., and Eric A. Johnson. *Improving Range Conditions For Wartime Livestock Production.* USDA Soil Conservation Service, Farmers Bull., No. 1921, 1942.

Talbot, M. W. *Indicators of Southwestern Range Conditions.* U. S. Forest Service, 1924.

Woolfolk, E. J., David F. Costello, and B. W. Allred. *The Major Range Types.* Yearbook of Agriculture, "Grass," 1948.

State:

Jones, John H., H. Schmidt, R. E. Dickson, J. M. Jones, J. K. Riggs, A. R. Kemmerer, P. E. Howe, W. H. Black, N. R. Ellis, and Paul T. Marion. *Vitamin "A" Studies in Fattening Feeder Calves and Yearlings.* Texas Agriculture Exp. Sta. Bull. 630, 1943.

Neale, Phillip E. *Nutrition In Relation To The Utilization Of Range Forage.* New Mexico Agriculture Exp. Sta. Bull. No. 910, 1940.

Nelson, A. B., C. H. Herbel, and H. M. Jackson. *Chemical Composition Of Forage Species Grazed By Cattle On An Arid New Mexico Range.* New Mexico Agriculture Exp. Sta. Bull. No. 561, 1970.

Pope, L. S., F. H. Baker, and R. W. MacVicar. *Vitamin "A" Studies With Beef Cattle.* Oklahoma State University, Bull. B-578, 1961.

Watkins, W. E. *The Calcium And Phosphorus Content Of Important New Mexico Range Forages.* New Mexico Agriculture Exp. Sta. Tech. Bull. 246, 1937.

Youngblood, B., and A. B. Cox. *An Economic Study Of A Typical Ranching Area On The Edwards Plateau Of Texas.* Texas Agriculture Exp. Sta. Bull. No. 297, 1922.

SPECIAL MONOGRAPHS:

Clements, Fredrick E. *Investigations In Ecology, 1928 And 1932.* Carnegie Institution of Washington. Reprints from Yearbooks No. 27, pages 188–196, and No. 31, pages 211–217.

Dyksterhuis, E. J. *The Vegetation Of The Fort Worth Prairie* and *The Vegetation Of The Western Cross Timbers*. Ecological Monographs, Vol. 16:1–29, Jan., 1946, and Vol. 18:325–376, July, 1948.

ARTICLES:

Branson, Farrel A. "Two New Factors Affecting Resistance to Grazing," *Journal of Range Management,* Vol. 6, No. 3, May, 1953.

Weaver, J. E., and Farrel A. Branson. "Quantitative Study of Degeneration of Mixed Prairie," *The Botanical Gazette,* Vol. 14, No. 4, June, 1953.

Weaver, J. E. "Underground Plant Development in Its Relation to Grazing," *Ecology,* Vol. 11, pages 543–57.

INDEX